W9-BNH-969

ALMOST PERFECT MURDERS

MINI-MYSTERIES FOR YOU TO SOLVE

HY CONRAD

Illustrated by Lucy Corvino

Sterling Publishing Co., Inc.
New York

To J. J.,
the love of my life

Edited by Jeanette Green

Library of Congress Cataloging-in-Publication Data

Conrad, Hy.
    Almost perfect murders : mini-mysteries for you to solve / Hy
Conrad; illustrated by Lucy Corvino.
        p.   cm.
    Includes index.
    ISBN 0-8069-9513-0
    1. Puzzles.   2. Detective and mystery stories.   3. Literary
recreations.   I. Title.
GV1507.D4C667   1997
793.73—dc21   96-50120

5   7   9   10   8   6
Published by Sterling Publishing Company, Inc.
387 Park Avenue South, New York, N.Y. 10016
© 1997 by Hy Conrad
Illustrations © 1997 by Lucy Corvino
Distributed in Canada by Sterling Publishing
% Canadian Manda Group, One Atlantic Avenue, Suite 105
Toronto, Ontario, Canada M6K 3E7
Distributed in Great Britain and Europe by Cassell PLC
Wellington House, 125 Strand, London WC2R 0BB, England
Distributed in Australia by Capricorn Link (Australia) Pty Ltd.
P.O. Box 6651, Baulkham Hills, Business Centre, NSW 2153,
Australia

Sterling ISBN 0-8069-9513-0

Contents

Acknowledgments

Writing a mystery puzzle is often like wrapping an awkwardly shaped package (a surprise present, if you will) and just barely having enough paper. You cover up one corner only to find another corner suddenly exposed. After a while you have no idea. Is it too obvious what's inside the wrapping paper? Does it look at all neat? Or is it the sloppy mess you suspect?

In composing this book, I have been blessed with three rewrappers, Jeff Clinard, Ray Kuehne, and Margaret Lashua, dedicated but critical mystery addicts whom I've never had the pleasure of meeting face-to-face. Throughout the years, their enthusiastic efforts have covered up countless exposed corners and kept me excited about the genre. They are, in short, the perfect fans.

I owe a special debt of gratitude to Jeff Clinard, who has been unfailingly reliable and insightful. In story after story, Jeff has outlined his own reasoning processes, much more logical than my own, congratulated me on my subtle (often unintentional) nuances, suggested easy, effective fixes to logic flubs and, most importantly, been kind. If Jeff ever decides to write mystery puzzles instead of repairing them, I will have to retire.

Introduction to Murder

It is said that authors write for themselves, creating the very works they would most like to read. In my case that's true. I have always been a fan of the whodunit. As a child, I was devoted to watching Perry Mason and reading Agatha Christie. World-famous authors, though many miles and decades away, were pitting themselves against me. We had a deal going. They would agree to play fair with the clues, and I would pledge not to sneak a peek at the end or to read the last chapter before making a good-faith effort to solve the crime.

It was years later that I developed a taste for character, mood, and ideas in my recreational reading. But our first loves are our deepest, and my heart will always hold a special place for the elegantly enigmatic plot twist.

In *Almost Perfect Murders*, I have devised thirteen diabolical murders, placing them in settings from Australia to Mexico to Transylvania. I've carefully laid out the clues, giving readers as much or as little help as they want in putting the pieces together.

At the end of each mystery are three questions to answer if you want to beat me at my own game. After these questions I give the minimum number of clues needed by the most skilled detectives. Each case has five clues, which you can examine in the order you decide. Don't be upset if you need to examine all five. For many of these cases, I would need them all myself.

Following these stories and clues is "Analysis of Evidence." In this section, I review the evidence for each case, point out the most intriguing clues, and try to emphasize the best mental direction for you to take. The cases appear in alphabetical order.

The solutions are at the end of the book, also in alphabetical order.

Now that I've told you how to use the book, I may as well tell you how to read it. Take your time. Get involved with the clues. Savor each case as if it were a mystery novel. There's usually a twist clever enough to be worth your while.

Death Takes a Ski Weekend

GRETEL AROMA WAS not in a good mood. The millionaire cosmetics queen and her husband had invited their four most snobbish friends to weekend at their chalet in the Swiss Alps. Shortly after the couples arrived, a blizzard hit, quickly burying the roads in half a meter of snow. That in itself was good. The chalet had plenty of provisions and the snowfall was welcomed. But then, bright and early on Saturday, one of Gretel's guests died of a heart attack. Gretel considered this a great inconvenience.

Paulina Chadwick had hopped on the stationary bicycle, warming up for a day on the slopes. An hour later, when two of the men found her, she was splayed across the handlebars. Hansel Aroma telephoned the nearest village and was told a hearse would come and claim the body. "Tonight, Herr Aroma. Or tomorrow—as soon as the road is plowed. Our condolences to you."

No one skied that day. Late that afternoon, Gretel sat in the lounge with her only living female guest, Belle Stuttgart. "I hope you don't mind her being in the bedroom next to yours," Gretel said. "We had no other place to put her."

"Of course not." Belle wrinkled her nose and checked her watch. "I can't believe poor Paulina. I'm almost her age. We're not that different. If she has a heart attack . . ."

Belle's husband approached from the Stuttgart's bedroom, interrupting this rare moment of reflection. Boris Stuttgart had no sooner arrived than his wife checked her watch again. Nearly six o'clock. "I think I need some fresh air," Belle said nervously and wandered out into the main hall.

Ten minutes later, Boris led Gretel and the chalet's handyman to the Stuttgart room at the back of the main floor. "There's this leaky pipe under our sink," he explained as he unlocked the door. The bedroom was cluttered with Belle's amazing array of beauty aids. Glancing between the bald heads of two wig stands, Gretel was the first to see the body. There in a corner she lay, face down in her sexiest robe, her flowing blond hair almost hiding the rope of pantyhose tied around her neck. It seemed that Belle Stuttgart had been murdered.

Gretel knelt down and felt the cold hand. "Oh, Belle!" she cried. "No! No! This ruins the whole weekend."

Boris pulled the hostess away, warning her not to touch anything. They left the room, locked the door, then telephoned the police. "We're sending two officers on skis," the efficient Swiss constable informed her.

Gretel turned from the phone to see Peter Chadwick. He had just come in and was removing a pair of snowshoes. "Road's still closed," he announced, his nerves frayed almost to the breaking point. "Having my wife just lying around . . . Hansel should put pressure on the authorities. Where is Hansel? Is he still on that business call?"

Gretel did her best to calm him, while Boris, the most recent widower, went off for a walk in the woods. When the police skied up half an hour later, they found Gretel waiting. "Thank heaven you're here. We didn't tell a soul about this unpleasantness," she whispered as she unlocked the bedroom door.

Wearing gloves, the constable in charge turned the victim's head. "Yes, that's Belle," the hostess said. "Hmm, strangulation does cruel things to one's complexion."

They began with an inspection. "The terrace is unlocked," the second officer said, then looked through the glass door. "There are lots of footprints outside. And . . ." He bent over and picked up a note that lay half-hidden under the corpse's left hip.

"My dearest Belle." The note had been typed. "Meet me at the usual spot. I'll be there between 6:00 and 6:30. Be discreet, my darling. The last thing we want is for our mates to find out."

"Very interesting," the straight-laced officer said. And he blushed.

Whodunit? (1) Who killed Belle Stuttgart? (2) How was it done? (3) What was the motive?

EVIDENCE *This case can be solved in two clues.*

Autopsy Reports
On the Monday after the deaths, the medical examiner from the village of Hautenberg performed autopsies on both corpses and came to these conclusions: Paulina Chadwick was killed by a massive coronary, possibly stemming from a previously undiagnosed heart murmur. Belle Stuttgart died of asphyxiation, the result of strangulation with a length of nylon pantyhose. She had been attacked from behind.

Police Report
"The victim had been attacked from the rear and was able to put up only a minimal struggle. The body was warm to the touch, indicating that death had occurred less than an hour prior to our arrival. The deceased was dressed in undergarments and a black silk robe. The garments and coat she had been wearing when last seen were hanging in the closet. As was her habit, Frau Stuttgart was wearing a blond wig. Two wig stands were found on the bureau, one empty and one holding a slightly shorter version of the same hairstyle."

Gretel's Testimony
"Belle had thin, rather unattractive hair and always wore extravagant blond wigs, though she didn't think we knew. She owned two versions of the same hairstyle, one "just-cut" and one grown out a bit. When I last saw her in the lounge, Belle was wearing the shorter wig. When Boris and I found her body, I could have sworn she had on the longer one, but I could be wrong."

Alibis
Between 6 P.M., the time Frau Stuttgart was last seen alive, and 6:10, the time Herr Stuttgart and Frau Aroma discovered the body, Peter Chadwick claimed to be snowshoeing from the chalet to the public road and back. A local farmer attested to seeing a man fitting his description in that area at 6:05.

During the same ten minutes, Hansel Aroma claimed to be in his office on the phone. "It was a prearranged conference call with our board of directors. It began a few minutes before six and lasted until Gretel came and found me a few minutes before seven."

A servant in the lounge testified that Herr Stuttgart and Frau Aroma had been there together until the handyman arrived and the three set off for the bedroom.

Search of the Grounds

A constable examined the relatively fresh snow. "Snowshoe tracks go from the chalet to the road and back, just as Herr Chadwick claimed." A set of tracks matching the boots of the deceased lead from the chalet out to the woods and the unoccupied caretaker's cottage. Another larger set of tracks also go from the chalet to the cottage. Both the larger and smaller set of tracks return to the chalet, side by side, entering through the Stuttgart's terrace door. The terrace, which is shared by this guest room and the one next door, is a mass of jumbled prints.

There is one additional set of large footprints. They go from the terrace around the side of the chalet, reentering by the front door.

Twice Terminated

DINSMORE, YOU'RE FIRED." Ellen O'Connor paused dramatically, then managed to spoil the moment with a sneeze. "Hazel told me how you've been toying with her affections. I'll have none of that in my house."

The sullen groundskeeper sneezed back, then glared from across the properly Irish library. "It was Mr. O'Connor who hired me, not you."

"Well, it's my house, not Mr. O'Connor's. Besides, I already talked to him. He's on his way home now." She opened her checkbook and began writing. "Here's your severance, Dinsmore. I want you off the property tonight."

Several hours later, the O'Connors sat on the verandah enjoying a cocktail as they gazed out over the lawns. "I hope I did the right thing. Dinsmore was a good groundskeeper but I never did trust him. And now with this Hazel business . . ."

"You were quite justified," James O'Connor assured his wife. "You know . . ." He was interrupted by the tinny wail of a car horn. "Sounds like Dinsmore's clunker. I thought he'd be gone by now." When the wail refused to cease, O'Connor put down his drink and walked off in the direction of the groundskeeper's cottage.

The old car sat idling in front of the locked-up cottage. The trunk was full of luggage and the large, bulky form of Paddy Dinsmore was behind the wheel, his head pressing against the horn bar as he convulsed in the final throws of an agonizing death.

The police drove through the gates of O'Connor Manor with no sirens. They knew how to be discreet. Mrs. O'Connor's family had been prominent in this area for centuries. When a quick forensic examination revealed the possibility of poison, the captain in charge sent the body off in an unmarked car, then set about taking statements. Discreetly, of course.

Ellen O'Connor described her afternoon. "James telephoned me from Dublin airport. He gave his approval to dismiss Dinsmore and said he would be home within the hour. I asked him to pick up another bottle of liquid cold medicine. After firing Dinsmore, I looked through the window. He was walking back toward his cottage. That's the last I saw of him. I talked to Hazel about dinner, then went up to my room for a nap. I'm trying to shake this cold. About two hours later I woke up and called James on the intercom. He was in the pool house, swimming laps. I asked him to join me for cocktails on the verandah. We were sitting there together when the car horn started up."

James O'Connor was slightly older than his wife, small, and spry. "I'd just returned from a business trip to Paris. Got in around six Paris time, five Greenwich time. Ellen was in her room napping. I went up to my own room, changed, then went downstairs to the pool and did an hour's worth of laps, until Ellen called on the intercom. I got dressed in the pool house and joined her on the verandah."

"So, you drove straight in from the airport?" the captain asked. "You never left the house and never saw Paddy Dinsmore?" Mr. O'Connor nodded.

The maid, Hazel, had been the only other person on the estate, and her story fit in nicely with the others'. "Mrs. O'Connor and I discussed the menu. She went upstairs and I began dinner. A half-hour later Mr. O'Connor drove up. Shortly after, I heard him in the pool house; it's connected to the mansion. As far as I know, neither of them went out."

The captain glanced around the kitchen and saw that it overlooked the sprawling lawns. "Did you see anyone at all while you were making dinner?"

"Well," Hazel hemmed. "I took a break and brought Mr. O'Connor a fresh towel. When I came back, I happened to look out. I thought I saw Paddy, Mr. Dinsmore, out on the lawn. I only saw him from the back, but it had to be him."

The captain went out for a walk and a think. "The man's not in the habit of eating in the mansion," he muttered softly. "He's just been fired and is about to go away forever. Yet someone goes to all the trouble to poison him. Why? And how?"

Whodunit?   (1) Who poisoned Paddy Dinsmore? (2) How was it done?   (3) What was the motive?

EVIDENCE   *This case can be solved in two clues.*

Autopsy Report
A substantial amount of N-oxystrychnine acid was discovered in the stomach and in muscle fibers. Ingestion most likely occurred one-half to one hour before death. Strychnine is among the more painful poisons, causing acute spasms and muscle contractions shortly after ingestion until the moment of death.

Inflammation of nasal cavity, plus higher than normal amounts of mucous in chest and esophageal areas, indicate that the deceased was also suffering from a cold.

James O'Connor's Statement
In a second statement, taken the following day, O'Connor confirms part of his wife's testimony. "Yes. Ellen did ask me to pick up some cold medicine. Unfortunately, I forgot. I had a lot of things on my mind."

A check of Mrs. O'Connor's bathroom cabinet shows a bottle of liquid cold medication, one-fourth full.

Search of the Cottage
The one-bedroom cottage is nearly completely stripped, including bedsheets and towels belonging to O'Connor Manor. All that's left are the bed, a few lamps, furnishings, and a telephone. In a bathroom wastebasket are found a disposable razor, twenty-two used tissues, and the packaging and the directions page for a liquid cold medicine. No bottle of medicine is found, nor is any safety seal.

Search of the Car
In trunk: Three suitcases filled with Paddy Dinsmore's possessions, including towels and bedsheets. The locks on two of the suitcases have been broken, probably with the small crowbar also found in the trunk.

In glove compartment: A small man's diamond ring and the deceased's wallet. In the wallet are 296 Irish punts and a severance check signed by Mrs. O'Connor.

Paddy's Dinsmore's Personal Effects

On the victim's right ring finger is a gold-plated ring with a chipped onyx stone. On his left wrist is an expensive watch. Across the leather band, two holes above the clasp, is a deep horizontal crease. The watch appears to be in good working order; however, the time is wrong. It reports the time as 65 minutes later than it actually is.

Attack of the Werewolf

TIM JOHNSON COULDN'T believe he was actually here, in his ancestral village in the Carpathian Mountains of Transylvania. It was like something from an old horror movie, this rustic tavern, not to mention the four sturdy villagers gathered around him. "You all knew my grandpa?" the wide-eyed American asked. "What was he like?"

Tim's cousin, Eric Havardi, was the local blacksmith. "Your mother's father was longtime party leader," he said in a heavy Romanian accent. "Good man."

Tim smiled. "Grandpa and I started corresponding back when I was a kid. I never found out; how did he die?"

The old, beamed tavern was suddenly silent. The woman, Marie Pularis, finally spoke. "Werewolf," she whispered. "Six years ago in the forest. Night of the full moon. His throat is slashed open."

Dr. Ionescu saw the shock in Tim's eyes. "It was a jagged knife, not a wolf," he said, glaring at Marie. "We found Werner alive but could not stop the bleeding."

"The werewolf strikes a wound that doesn't heal," said the last member of the group. Gregor Pularis was Marie's brother and the village mayor. "Your grandfather killed a werewolf once. Now all of his line are cursed."

"Wow! I guess I'd better watch my step." Tim laughed nervously and changed the subject. Reaching into his backpack, he brought out a leather-bound book. "Grandpa sent me this. He had a premonition of doom. He said there were things in life he regretted and he wanted me to know. Trouble is, it's in Romanian. It's his diary. I was hoping one of you . . ."

"Diary?" Marie instantly held out her hand. "I am so happy to do translation."

Eric Havardi stopped her. "Your English is no good, Marie. Maybe in morning we go to priest. He has good English and plenty of time. Yes?"

"Sounds like a good idea." Tim put the diary back in his pack. "Well, it was a long drive." He wished everyone a good night and headed out toward his grandfather's cottage.

The foursome watched him walk down the wooded lane, illuminated by the glow of a full moon. "Poor fellow." Gregor shook his head as a pack of wolves howled in the distance.

"You are superstitious fools," Dr. Ionescu growled, then marched off in the direction of his own cottage. The others stayed on for several more drinks, toasting the misguided descendant of Werner Havardi. At 11:45, the torrential rains started, sending the three villagers scurrying back to their homes.

The church clock had just struck midnight when the wolves howled again. Two boys were on the road, returning from a dance in a nearby town. They saw the cottage and the wolves circling by the open door. Scaring away the wolves with rocks, the boys rushed inside. There on the hearth was the body of Tim Johnson. The blood surrounding the gash in his throat was still liquid. The boys touched nothing, but ran off to find the mayor and doctor.

By the next morning, the skies had cleared. Gregor, the mayor, was leading an officer from the rural militia to the cottage. "The doctor and I made sure he was dead. Then we telephoned you," Gregor said as he threw open the unlocked door. But the body was gone. Not even the blood remained, only the stain of it on the floor.

The corpse was discovered later that morning in the river at the base of a small waterfall. When the townsfolk pulled the American to shore, they were shocked to find all the major veins and arteries slashed open. "The werewolf," Marie Pularis hissed. "It wanted all of his blood." And she made the sign of the cross.

Whodunit? (1) Who or what killed Tim Johnson? (2) What was the motive? (3) Why was the body moved and the veins slashed?

EVIDENCE   *This case can be solved in two clues.*

Boys' Testimony

"There were only two wolves, not a full pack. They circled by the door, excited, like they wanted to go in. We pelted them with rocks and scared them off. Matthias and I were careful. Before going in, we checked the mud outside. There were no human footprints. Just wolf prints. Between the moonlight and the glow from the fireplace, we could see. The American was on the floor by the hearth. We went close but didn't touch. Blood was glistening in the wound. We're hunters. We knew the kill had to be fresh, no more than fifteen minutes, I'd say. We left right away to find the mayor."

Search of the Cottage

Report from the first officer on the scene: "On our arrival, there was no blood on the floor. Whatever was used to wipe it up had been disposed of. There were few signs of struggle, suggesting the American was overpowered or taken by surprise. A search of his possessions revealed the usual items of personal clothing plus a guide book, local map, a wallet filled with money and credit cards, passport, airplane ticket, car key, key ring, a book in English, and a suitcase. In the bathroom was a toiletry kit containing, among other things, three disposable syringes, three vials of sterilized water, and three vials of a white powder labeled Factor VIII."

Alibis

Dr. Ionescu: "I left the tavern about 10:30, going straight to my house where I live alone. Shortly before the eleven o'clock chime, young Tristan came for me. His mother was giving birth. I was at their cottage until sometime after midnight, when the mayor came to fetch me. It was a girl, by the way."

Gregor Pularis: "When the rains started, I ran for home. My wife was already asleep and I didn't wake her. I put on a kettle for tea and had a cup. I was just changing out of my wet clothes when the boys knocked on my door. I went to get the doctor before we all headed out to Werner's old cottage."

Marie Pularis: "My cottage is far from the tavern. About halfway there, I changed my mind. I ducked into the church, hoping to wait out the rain. It wasn't letting up, so I finally had no choice but to run. My husband says I came in a few minutes after midnight.

Eric Havardi: "I ran from the tavern to my own cottage. It is just down the road from where my American cousin was staying. I could see his window from my window. The light was flickering in his fireplace. Other than that, I saw nothing and heard nothing. Not until the wolves started howling."

Village Gossip
After interviewing the village women, the militia pieced together the following. "Werner Havardi was a frightened, sickly man who hated knives. They say that's why he never shaved, out of fear of razors. He was the local party leader and greatly respected. In all the confusion following the fall of Communism, a large cache of party funds vanished from local coffers. It was thought that Werner and a cohort engineered the theft, but nothing could ever be proved. Not long after the accusations, Werner was killed by a wolf."

Autopsy
The rural militia is not equipped to conduct a modern autopsy, but an examination of the body revealed: "The victim was in his early twenties and seemed unathletic by our standards. Cause of death was a cut jugular vein, the wound created by a jagged knife or by slashing claws. The other wounds were similar in shape, all delivered after death. Severed radial arteries in each wrist, severed femoral veins and arteries in each leg, severed subclavian veins and arteries in the upper arms, a slashed carotid artery, and stomach slashes that cut open the vena cava. The body had been in the water for at least six hours. It will be transported to Bucharest as soon as possible."

Death of a Dummy

GENT GLEASON ANSWERED the doorbell and warmly ushered the three friends into his apartment. "There's no water, I'm afraid. Water-main break this whole side of Prague. I had just enough of the bottled stuff to make coffee." The four intelligence officers were officially assigned to the U.S. Embassy. Once a week they met socially for drinks, dessert, and—not poker, that was too uncerebral a pursuit—contract bridge. The evenings were rotated among their homes in the old section of Prague, as was the responsibility for dessert.

Gleason's guests accepted the lack of water with humor. Levy contributed the expected bathroom jokes, then unveiled a cake topped with red marshmallow frosting and a candied cherry. "My wife made it; so, no cracks."

"I thought it was my week," Morales said, placing a bag on the counter. "I bought some Czech pastries, Gleason's favorite. What am I saying? He'll chow down anything. Hey, congratulations, Gleason, if I haven't said it before."

The heavyset Gleason had just been promoted to Internal Security. This secretive branch had the directive to root out moles and counterspies throughout Eastern Europe, still a hotbed of espionage despite the end of the Cold War. Morales himself had been up for the post and competition had been fierce. "So, did you get briefed yet?" Morales teased. "You know, all those telltale ways of ferreting out moles: vaccination scars, dental work, old tattoos."

Levy was the director of Internal Security and put an end to the shoptalk. "That's on a need-to-know basis. Let's play. Dessert and coffee after the first rubber."

The fourth player, Paterno, was Gleason's best friend, in or out of the embassy. Gleason and Paterno grabbed beers from the refrigerator and sat down to play against Levy (scotch on the rocks) and Morales (coffee, black). In keeping with their routine, the bridge table was set up with one deck instead of the usual two, giving them a little more time between hands.

The cards fell evenly and the first rubber took over an hour. At some point in the proceedings each of the four men was dummy, the nonplaying partner. In each case, the dummy took advantage of his break, getting up to stretch his legs or refill his drink. Morales had just warmed up his coffee and picked up another beer for Gleason when Levy put down his cards with a frown. "These are sticky. Time for a new deck."

Gleason, the host, gathered up the old cards, dropped them into a wastebasket, then went and fished around in a sideboard drawer. "Here we are. I knew I had one." Gleason tossed the unopened box to Paterno, who unwrapped it and began to shuffle.

Gleason stretched his arms and wandered away from the table. A minute later, just as he was crossing back to join the others, the overweight agent began to breathe heavily. Sweat dripped from his brow. He swayed, then collapsed to the floor. Special Agent Gleason was dead.

Despite their familiarity with death, the three agents couldn't believe the obvious signs. For several minutes, they tried reviving the dead man. Finally, following a nasty hunch, Levy bent down over the corpse of his newly appointed assistant and smelled his breath. "Cyanide," he muttered.

"Cyanide?" echoed Paterno. "That's impossible. How? What the heck was he eating?"

"Are you kidding?" Morales said. "Gleason? The human vacuum? God only knows what he's been munching."

Paterno pushed Levy aside and vainly tried to resuscitate his friend. "Must be a heart attack. It can't be . . . I mean, if it's cyanide, then that means one of us . . ." He left the sentence unfinished.

"Yes," agreed Morales with startling frankness. "Either it's suicide or one of us."

Whodunit? (1) Who killed Agent Gleason? (2) How was the poison administered? (3) What clue fingers the killer?

EVIDENCE   *This case can be solved in three clues.*

Autopsy Report

Death was caused by sodium cyanide and probably occurred within one to three minutes of ingestion. Even for someone of the deceased's size and weight, as little as four grains could have been effectively used. An undissolved granule of sodium cyanide was discovered stuck between two left molars and indicates the poison had been administered in granular form rather than dissolved in a solution.

Levy's Testimony

"I basically knew Gleason from our weekly bridge games, not much more. He'd just been promoted to my department, Internal Security, but hadn't yet started. Paterno and Gleason were best friends. They regularly took vacations together, usually to the Adriatic beaches with girlfriends. Morales and Gleason had been rivals for this new job, but that's no reason to kill anyone. Why was Gleason chosen over Morales? I suppose the main reason was dedication. Gleason seemed more dedicated to the 'firm.' "

Search of the Kitchen

The presence of seven identical Czech pastries and a single empty doily point to the possibility that the deceased ate the eighth. The field of red marshmallow icing covering the cake appears undisturbed. The dish towel seems slightly sticky. Pastries, cake icing, towel, beer bottles, and glasses were all removed for testing.

A small, crumpled glassine envelope was found in the kitchen trash. Interior is coated with minute granular residue (white). Removed for testing.

Analysis of Food and Drink

Samples taken from beer bottles, glasses, dish towel, cake icing, and pastries. Tested for hydrogen cyanide and derivatives. Minute traces of sodium cyanide discovered on dish towel. Other results all negative.

Examination of the Card Table

A half-dealt deck of playing cards is found on the table. Many fronts and backs are slightly sticky. A playing card box is near the table center. Four coasters, no ashtrays, scoring pad, and pencil. All beer bottles, empty or full, were taken in for testing as was the pencil lead.

The Bee All and End All

THE *DAILY COURIER* was hoping to call it "The A B C D Murder" in honor of Ace, Beatrice, Cecil, and Divine. The four alphabetical suspects were all nieces and nephews of the victim, Lord Alexander Purdy. But by the time a clever writer thought this up, one of the group had already been arrested and the headline had to be scratched. Luckily, the British tabloid was able to come up with something just as good: "DID TYCOON DIE FROM BEA'S STING?"

The details turned out to be as sensational as the headline. It all began on a sunny afternoon when the aging industrialist gathered his four relations together for an alfresco lunch at his Sussex estate. The four cousins spent the morning roaming the grounds and communing with nature. At noon, the housekeeper dished up an extravagant picnic in the gazebo and afterwards, Uncle Alexander partook of his ritual nap in the hammock beside the garden shed.

From the columned porch, Ace, Cecil, and Divine gazed out over the lawn. "What is Beatrice trying to do?" Ace wondered.

The others could see it, too. Cousin Beatrice was standing by the hammock, waving her hands skittishly, running a few feet away from her sleeping uncle, then running back. "She'd better not disturb the old man."

Suddenly Lord Purdy sat up, grabbing his elbow. A light breeze carried his cries of help to the porch and within seconds, the cousins were racing across the lawn. "Bee sting," the millionaire gasped and nearly fell out of the hammock. Uncle, as they all knew, was severely allergic to bees and had been hospitalized on two previous occasions.

"I tried to shoo them away," Beatrice moaned. "But they just got more excited."

Ace, Beatrice, and Cecil bundled their uncle into the Range Rover and rushed off for the hospital, leaving Divine to telephone the family doctor. Divine was still at the estate two hours later when Cecil telephoned. "Looks like the old man survived this one. Ace, Bea, and I have been taking turns sitting by his bedside and . . . Hold on a minute." The phone went dead for not one minute but several. Then Cecil's shaky voice came back on. "Uncle Purdy's dead. Blasted bees. He should've had them fumigated like we've been telling him."

Lord Purdy's physician was suspicious from the outset, and before the cousins even left the hospital, he expressed his concern. "Bee stings usually kill within an hour, not two. I'm going to order an autopsy."

Beatrice and Cecil took taxis to their own homes that afternoon, leaving Ace to drive the Range Rover back to the estate. Over a dinner of picnic leftovers, he repeated the doctor's words to Divine. "He suspects murder," Ace concluded with a quiver in his voice.

Divine nodded. "It has to be Beatrice," she said coolly. "I read about this. You fill a syringe with poison. If the person's asleep at the time, he might not even feel the injection. Then you just pinch his arm and blame it on a bee."

Before Ace could reason with her, Divine had left the house and was striding out to the hammock. Ace joined her and within five minutes they found it, a little wad of cloth stuffed up into the faucet by the garden shed. They knew better than to open it. Together they carried the wadded cloth into the house and called the local constabulary.

Divine's off-the-cuff theory seemed surprisingly accurate. The medical examiner came back with a verdict of death by poison. As for the wadded cloth, it contained a disposable syringe. Traces of formic acid were found in its cylinder.

The prosecutor presents all these facts in his opening argument. It looks like a clear-cut case against cousin Beatrice. Or is it?

Whodunit?   (1) Who killed Lord Purdy?   (2) How was the murder committed?   (3) When was it committed?

EVIDENCE   *This case can be solved in three clues.*

Autopsy Report

"Death was caused by formic acid, a corrosive compound used in chemical processing. Its symptoms and strength are similar to those of bee venom. The acid wasn't swallowed. That would have caused damage to the pharynx and abdomen, which I didn't find. It was administered by syringe. There was a reddened area near the left elbow and we were able to identify two infection sites. In other words, two very tiny puncture marks."

Gardener's Testimony

"I last used the garden faucet at about 2:30 on the afternoon of Lord Purdy's death. Everyone but Miss Divine had gone off to the hospital. I connected the hose and used it to refill the reflecting pool. To the best of my recollection, the water flowed freely."

Syringe Evidence

Investigating Officer: "The murder weapon was a disposable syringe, similar to one that Dr. Purdy admitted to having in her medical bag. We asked to see Dr. Purdy's bag. It was in her car. Inside the bag we found the wrapper for a disposable syringe, the same brand as the murder weapon. Dr. Purdy had no explanation except to say that someone must have stolen the syringe earlier that day. No prints were found on the syringe."

Officer on the Scene

"Right from the start of my investigation I noticed a lot of bees swarming around the hammock. While inadvertently touching the underside of the hammock, I discovered a tacky substance. It turned out to be honey. Someone had spread honey all over the hammock bottom. That's what had attracted the bees."

Family Solicitor's Testimony

"Last month Dr. Beatrice Purdy came to London and took me to lunch. Over dessert, she asked if there was any way to talk her uncle into releasing part of her inheritance while he was still alive. She said she was concerned about death taxes. I told her that Lord Purdy disliked discussing his demise. He considered it unlucky, and bringing up the subject was more than my job was worth. To be honest, the other three cousins had approached me in the same way, each trying to get money. All I could tell them was that Lord Purdy had divided his assets evenly among them, and that they would inherit only on his death."

The Day of the Dead

IN THE COOL, pine-forested foothills southeast of Mexico City lay Hacienda del Sol. The estate was austere and proper yet somehow hospitable, much like its owner, Maria Monteneras. Maria, a national institution, was a multimedia earth mother, author of books like *Frugal Hospitality* and star of her own television series, "Entertaining with Mama Maria."

When Maria's beloved husband, Pepe, died, all Mexico grieved. It happened one night, after a small dinner party. A drunken Pepe Monteneras fell from a footbridge on the hacienda property and was dashed to death in the dry riverbed below. Rumors of suicide and murder circulated in the tabloid press, then quickly faded. A full year after Pepe's accident, Maria finally came out of her mournful seclusion.

Roberto Robles was Maria's agent and friend. He and his wife arrived Friday afternoon. They unpacked in one of the guest rooms, then strolled among the dusty olive trees. "How like Maria to mark her return to life with a weekend party," Inez Robles said in hushed admiration. Roberto grunted and frowned. "What's the matter with you?"

"Tomorrow's the Day of the Dead," Roberto said, referring to the Mexican observance of All Souls' Day. "It was exactly one year ago tomorrow that Pepe died. Why did she invite us?"

"She didn't want to be alone."

Roberto still frowned. "You, me, Hugo, Yolanda. We were all here last year, this same weekend. And now Maria invites us back, the same four who were here when Pepe died. I wonder . . ."

Hugo and Yolanda were sitting in the hacienda's homey kitchen also wondering. "I don't know why Maria took it all so hard," Hugo hissed a bit maliciously. "Everyone knew Pepe was philandering about. I'm surprised he died a natural death, what with jealous husbands, perhaps a mistress fed up with his promises . . ."

"Sh!" Yolanda warned her husband just in time. "Maria, dear. I can't believe you're entertaining a house full of guests all by yourself."

"Mama" Maria breezed into the kitchen. "As my publisher, you should know my methods, Yolanda." She was at the counter, already beginning to chop garlic. "Inez is a vegetarian. Hugo eats fish at every dinner; no red meat. Roberto has a milk allergy. If you plan ahead, being a good hostess isn't any more time-consuming or expensive. As for servants . . . Well, tomorrow is a holiday." She paused, cleaver poised in midair. "A day to remember our loved ones."

That evening, true to form, Maria served up a seemingly effortless feast. They were still laughing and talking long past midnight when Maria made the final toast. "To old friends, here and gone." She drank. "And now I must marinate tomorrow's dinner. Please enjoy yourselves." And she vanished into the kitchen.

Of the four guests, Inez rose earliest on Saturday morning to find breakfast pastries and strong coffee already brewing. A note on the stove announced, "I'm working in the cottage this morning. You all know where to find what you need. Perhaps this afternoon we'll go horseback riding. Maria."

By noon everyone was up and wandering the grounds. By two, they were growing restless. "I told her she had to finish the new book," Yolanda whined. "But I didn't think she'd do it on a holiday."

By three they were worried. Hugo and Roberto walked over to the work cottage. Even from a distance, through the pulled window curtain, they recognized the silhouette sitting at her writing table. "She's been in that same position for hours," Hugo said as he knocked. "Something's wrong." There was no answer.

Neither man knew what to expect when they broke down the cottage door. They certainly didn't expect to find what they did, a room empty except for a mannequin. The store dummy wore one of Maria's trademark wigs and was propped up in her chair.

The guests immediately set out to search, calling Maria's name at the top of their lungs. Yolanda was crossing the footbridge when she happened to remember Pepe's accident a year earlier. Reflexively, she glanced down into the dry riverbed below, then screamed.

Maria's lifeless, bloody body lay on the sun-bleached rocks. "Just like Pepe," Yolanda muttered to herself. "The Day of the Dead."

Whodunit? (1) Who killed Maria Monteneras? (2) What was the motive? (3) Maria accidentally left a clue pointing to her killer. What was it?

EVIDENCE *This case can be solved in two clues.*

Suspects' Actions and Alibis
At 1 P.M., the time when the attack presumably took place, all four suspects claimed to be in different areas of the estate. None of their alibis can be corroborated.

At the policía's request, all four suspects remained at the hacienda. On Saturday, Yolanda barbecued the three Argentinean beefsteaks left marinating from the night before. For herself, Inez grilled the prepared vegetables left in the refrigerator. For dessert there were three custard flans and a chilled fruit compote for Roberto. Even in death, Maria was the perfect hostess.

Note Found at the Scene
"Meet me on the footbridge at 1 P.M. Don't let anyone see you. And bring this note. I'll explain when you arrive." (*unsigned*)

The above was found in the pocket of the dress Maria was wearing. The writing is not yet identified, but it matches the handwriting on the note Maria supposedly left in the kitchen.

Scene of the Crime
Maria Monteneras had fallen through a hole in the bridge's wooden railing. An examination of the broken edges shows

that it had been sawed nearly through. A simple push would have been enough to break the railing.

The victim's clothing was torn.

Autopsy Report

"A preliminary examination places the time of death between noon and 2 P.M. on Saturday. Scratches on the arms and face attest to a struggle having taken place between the victim and her attacker."

Examination of Victim's Bedroom

In a locked bottom drawer, the police found a pile of canceled checks, all signed by Maria. The checks had all been made out to Confidential Results, a Mexico City firm of private investigators. The first was dated December 8, eleven months earlier. The checks were dated in regular intervals from December through late September. Also found was a small manila envelope labeled with the notation "please return." Inside the envelope was a hand-carved button with torn threads attached.

The Marquis de Sade's
Locked Room

THE DE SADE family had a long and noble history with one infamous exception, the Count Donatien Alphonse François, otherwise known as the Marquis de Sade. This 18th century author of scandalous novels had so shamed the family that they were still recovering 200 years later. So, when Professor Petit knocked on their door, claiming that their ancestor might have had a medical reason behind his sexual ravings, the de Sades were intrigued.

"There was a chemical imbalance in his brain," the bald, bespectacled professor said emphatically. "I've studied all the records from the asylums where he spent so much of his life. Now if I could just examine his private papers. They will confirm my theory."

"His private papers?" The current count frowned. "I'm afraid not. The family has done its best to keep his papers out of public hands. We once allowed a scholar into the bank vault to examine them. A month later, a newly discovered de Sade letter appeared at an auction house. Sold for quite a lot. We knew he'd stolen it. But we own thousands of these disgusting documents, very few of them cataloged. We couldn't prove it was ours."

The professor was crestfallen. And then he had an idea. "I can do my work right in the bank vault. Then every day as I leave, a guard can search me from head to foot."

Georges, the count's elder son, objected. "This is a trick. He's a thief, just like the other. The second he sees some document he can't live without, he'll stuff it up his sleeve."

Antoine, the younger son, disagreed. "Let's do it. If he can prove that the man who gave our family name to sadism was clinically ill, wouldn't that be worth a slight risk?"

The count agreed with Antoine and on the next Monday, the research began. Every morning, a guard at the Banque de Paris searched the professor, then ushered him into an inner room of the bank's highly secured vault. There he locked the professor inside with his briefcase and his lunch in a paper sack. Six hours later, the professor exited the vault and was searched again—lunch sack, briefcase, everything.

On Wednesday, the professor made an astonishing discovery. On Thursday, he showed it to the family. The guard did his usual job of searching the professor, then led him and the three de Sades into the vault's inner room. "Here," the professor said proudly and pointed to a letter, yellow with age but impeccably preserved.

"From Napoléon Bonaparte," Antoine said in awe. "To the marquis." The family huddled around the small page of notepaper. "Asking the marquis's advice about Napoléon's personal relationship with Joséphine. Amazing. This is worth a fortune."

The professor smiled. "The Emperor Napoléon asking the Marquis de Sade for romantic advice? I can't wait to publish this."

The count's embarrassment was mixed with pride. He thanked Professor Petit but steadfastly refused permission to reprint or sell the letter.

"Did you see the way he drooled?" Georges muttered as they left. "He knows the family will never part with it. We have to take precautions." That same day, Georges hired a private detective to check into the professor's background. He also warned the guard to be extra vigilant in his searches.

It was early the following Monday that the family received a report. "Professor Petit seems genuine," the detective informed them. "He is poor, even for a scholar. Although . . ." The detective cleared his throat. "Last Friday, his neighbors say he treated everyone to drinks at the neighborhood brasserie. They say he was spending quite freely."

"Friday?" Antoine said. "That's the day after he showed us the Napoléon letter."

"How did he suddenly get money?" the count asked. Before anyone could speculate, the phone rang. It was from the bank.

"The professor hasn't shown up this morning," the guard told them. "I telephoned his apartment, but there's no answer."

Antoine immediately set off for the professor's apartment,

while Georges rushed over to the bank. Entering the vault with the guard close behind, Georges went straight to the desk, set up in the middle of the inner room. He bent over to inspect the masses of paper. "Oh my Lord!" Turning around, he showed his find to the guard. It was the professor's calling card. On the blank side was a single handwritten word, "merci."

"Go call the police," Georges shouted. The guard obeyed, leaving Georges to search in vain for the missing letter.

As expected, the police didn't find Pierre Petit at his apartment. Hopes were not high on ever tracking down the absconding scholar. But then on Tuesday the manager of a seedy hotel in the Pigalle arrondisement unlocked Room 326 and found the professor. Strangled to death.

Whodunit?   (1) Who killed Professor Petit?   (2) Who stole the Napoleon letter?   (3) How did the thief remove the letter from the vault?

EVIDENCE   *This case can be solved in two clues.*

Interview of the Hotel Manager

"Sunday afternoon, a man came in with a false beard and a wig and without a suitcase. We don't ask questions here. He rented a room for two nights and he paid in advance. He wanted to come and go at night; so, I gave him a front-door key. He also said he didn't want maid service, which was fine with Yvette. I didn't see him again until Tuesday. It was well after the noon checkout time. I went up to his room. At first I didn't recognize the clean-shaven, bald man. (*He shivers.*) Strangulation. That's a pretty sadistic way to kill someone."

Autopsy Report

"The cause of death was ligature strangulation, the forceful closure of blood vessels and air passages of the throat. The neck area was covered with bruises, abrasions, and contusions, indicating that the victim had struggled. Deep rope abrasions on both wrists. A contusion on the rear of the head, delivered at least twenty-four hours prior to death.

"Time of death is estimated between midnight and 6:00 A.M. on Monday morning. The stomach was completely empty, indicating that the decedent had not eaten for at least six hours prior to his death."

Search of the Murder Scene

A wig and false beard were recovered from a corner of the hotel room and were identified by the manager as belonging to his mystery quest.

The room and bathroom were completely devoid of personal possessions. No suitcase, clothing, or toilet articles. There was no trace of the Napoléon letter.

Interview of the Guard

"I searched Professor Petit thoroughly each time, making him strip to his drawers and then frisking his drawers. I even checked his lunch sack and notebooks before he went in. I'd be willing to swear he didn't get anything by me. I'm good at my job.

"Every morning, the bank manager unlocked the vault. I would search the professor, then let him into the inner room, locking that door behind him. I stood guard outside the vault all day. Bank employees use the vault constantly, but no one could get inside the inner room, not until I unlocked it at the end of the day and frisked him again. For this second search, there was always another guard with me. Antoine de Sade insisted on this precaution.

"All Sunday night, I was at home in Malmaison, about 15 kilometers outside Paris. We had a sick baby; so my wife and I were up and down all night, taking care of him."

Interview of the Professor's Friends

The professor had no close friends. His acquaintances testified that he was usually broke, owing money to every merchant in the *quartier*. On Friday night, he showed up at Le Chat Noir, where he paid off his tab and treated everyone to a round of drinks. When asked about his new-found wealth, the professor said that an anonymous packet of money had been slipped under his door.

Neighbors assume the professor was killed in a robbery. They think someone saw him flashing his money and followed him to the seedy hotel.

River of No Return

THE MOUNTAINS OF Portugal are known for their steep gorges and stunning views, a perfect spot for hikers like Jan deWys, president of the deWys Trust, Holland's richest charitable foundation. Jan and his assistant, Margo, were combining business with pleasure, taking care of paperwork in the morning hours, then hiking throughout the beautiful summer afternoons.

It was Thursday, their last full day at the Pinhão Spa. They had just finished lunch with Gordon Armgaard, a fellow Netherlander they met just the day before. Gordon and the young millionaire had a lot in common and got along instantly.

"I know you have to get to the Lisbon airport," Jan said as Gordon packed up his rental car. "But you certainly have time for one last hike."

Margo, sensible as always, came up with the solution. "Gordon can drive us to the river trail. All three of us can hike for an hour or so. Gordon will drive to the airport from there, and we'll walk back. It's not very far."

Gordon finally agreed. They were getting into his red Renault when a voice stopped them. "Jan! What a coincidence." It was Sophia deWys, Jan's estranged wife, who was just emerging from a taxi with her luggage. "I had no idea you were here."

Jan seemed delighted by the encounter, but Margo did not. "What a coincidence," the middle-aged assistant echoed. "We were just leaving." And before anyone could object, Margo bundled her employer into the car, and they sped off.

Sophia spent her day by the pool, waiting for their return. Late that afternoon, she saw the two hikers coming down the trail. "We're exhausted," Margo called out from a distance. "Maybe we'll see you tomorrow at breakfast."

On Friday morning, Sophia got up early—early for her. It was 10 A.M. when the Italian-born beauty came down to the lobby, just in time to see Margo at the front desk, checking out. Sophia had hoped to spend a few minutes with her estranged husband, but Jan was nowhere to be found. By the time Sophia wandered out the main door, it was too late. All she saw was the back of his head as he drove off in the rented Mercedes. Margo, in the passenger seat, turned around, saw Sophia in the doorway, and smiled triumphantly.

Early that afternoon, the Mercedes arrived at Vimioso. As the crow flew, the picturesque village was only 30 kilometers from Pinhão, but upstream and on the other side of the Douro River. The rocky, twisting roads made the trip into a 3-hour ordeal. Despite the miserable drizzle, Jan deWys decided on some exercise. At 2:30, he approached the concierge and asked for a hiking map. "My assistant doesn't want to go with me," he explained with a cheery shrug. The millionaire adjusted his sunglasses and waved good-bye to Margo, who was in the lounge having tea.

"Was that Mr. deWys?" the Englishwoman next to her inquired. Margo nodded. They had introduced themselves only a few minutes earlier and were exchanging small talk. Gloria Westin and her husband both worked for International Infant Charities. "Wait till I tell my Horace," Gloria gushed. "For years, we've been trying to get a meeting with Jan deWys. Horace is out hiking, too. Maybe they'll run into each other."

The Westins never got their meeting. That evening, when Jan deWys still hadn't returned, Margo raised the alarm. Other hikers had seen deWys hiking off by himself, but no one had seen him after 3 P.M.

It was late the next morning when a female hiker came across his belongings. Off the narrow trail, along a steep slope, she found the sunglasses and his monogrammed walking stick. Scuff marks and broken twigs led to the edge of a cliff. A hundred feet below, Jan deWys's backpack had latched itself onto a branch in the middle of the deep, swiftly flowing Douro.

For two days the police searched, going downstream farther and farther until they found him. Jan's bloated remains were lodged between a pair of boulders in the middle of the river, a kilometer from the Douro bridge, and an amazing twenty-five kilometers from the spot where he'd fallen in.

"No. Not fallen in," the local doctor told the police officials. "Hit over the head and pushed in." He showed them the contusion and explained the evidence. "Clearly a case of murder."

Whodunit? (1) Who killed Jan deWys? (2) What was the motive? (3) How did the killer hope to fool the police?

EVIDENCE   *This case can be solved in three clues.*

Sophia's Testimony
"My being here was no coincidence. I needed to talk to Jan about living arrangements—like my allowance. Since our separation, I've had next to nothing to live on.

"That witch Margo always kept me away—first this secret trip, then managing to avoid me. I found out their next stop was Vimioso. I got here by taxi. I didn't want to give her the chance to evade me again; so, that Friday I planted myself outside the main gate, the only gate. That was around two. I was hoping Jan would go hiking. There were several other people who came and left, but he never exited the gate. At about five, I gave up."

The deWys Trust Records
An investigation of the deWys Trust showed five separate checks made out to Infant Philanthropies, a London-based charity. The checks totaled 3.4 million in British pounds. Although the organization had a London post office box and bank account, there is no other evidence of the charity's existence. The account for Infant Philanthropies is empty and the name used to open it, Harry Weinholt, appears to be an alias.

Hunters' Testimony
The police asked residents and tourists alike to come forward and report any unusual sightings. Two peasants responded. For several days, they had been hunting grouse by the Douro bridge, the only local span across the river. Late on Thursday

afternoon, they sighted a red Renault parked behind a clump of rocks, one hundred meters from the road. Early Friday afternoon, the car was still there. By Saturday, however, it was gone.

Crime Scene Report

In recreating the murder, the police concluded that it would have been nearly impossible for a body falling from the cliff to hit a portion of the Douro River deep enough to send it floating downstream. This led police to two possible theories: (1) The body was physically thrown from the cliff. (2) After the body fell from the cliff, it was moved into the center of the river. Neither theory seems completely satisfactory.

Autopsy Report

"The body was found securely lodged between two boulders in the middle of the Douro. It seemed to be mere luck that it had been stopped in this spot and not in one of the dozens of other log jams or outcroppings.

"Although the body had been damaged and deteriorated by water and other natural elements, both Sophia deWys and Margo Apsed made positive identifications. In addition, the corpse's fingerprints match those of Jan deWys, on file with the Dutch National Registrar's Office."

The Baffling Break-ins

HE FIRST ONE occurred on a Friday. At 11:42 A.M., a silent alarm was triggered, alerting the police of Adelaide, South Australia, of a break-in at 210 Eucalyptus Lane. A squad car was dispatched. Arriving at the suburban residence, the officers found a splintered door frame, but no other signs of a burglary. The homeowner was notified and immediately came home from work.

"Nothing's missing," Doug Atkins reported. "I keep me a careful inventory of valuables. Not a gnat's hair is out of place. Lucky us, no one was home. The kids are in summer camp and my wife's visiting her family's station in the outback."

The very next morning, Saturday, at 11:35 A.M., it happened again. The silent alarm at the Atkins's house was once again triggered. The patrol officers arrived and again found the door forced. As before, nothing was missing. "If this ocker is looking for something, he's very neat," observed a patrolman. "Not a speck of dust seems to be disturbed."

On the third day, Atkins made a show of getting into his car and driving off to church. By 11 A.M., he had sneaked back and set up his own lookout post directly across the street. Atkins found an angle that gave him an unencumbered view of his own door. But no one came. His trap hadn't worked.

On Monday morning at 11:41, the intruder struck again. This time, Doug Atkins was prepared. He had hidden a camera just inside the living-room door, giving himself a video of the inner half of the entry hall and of the second-floor staircase. But even this proved futile. The sound of the break-in was duly recorded, but no intruder ever walked in front of the camera's line of sight.

"This blighter's toying with me," Atkins growled. "The next time he comes . . ." But there wasn't to be a next time. The door was never again forced and the alarm never again went off.

This odd little crime spree was made even more notable by the victim's occupation. Doug Atkins, as it happened, was Adelaide's well-respected police chief, and his colleagues throughout the territory were having a good, long laugh at

Chief Atkins's expense.

A week after the last break-in, he received a note in the mail. "Chief Atkins, For the past couple months, you've been doing your best to get the goods on me. I guess I finally outsmarted you. Sorry I had to break into your home to do it." *Signed:* Still at large.

"Well, at least this provides some motive," Atkins mused. "Whoever broke in was somehow trying to escape arrest."

Atkins decided to review his unsolved cases and found three that fit the bill, cases that he had personally pursued over the previous two months.

Case #1: *Robbery and Murder.* The safe of the Second Baptist Church had been broken into and $100,000 of the building fund stolen. In the process, a church janitor was shot to death, having been in the wrong place at the wrong time. Chief Atkins suspected the robber/killer of having inside help. The Reverend Billy Green was the prime suspect and had been interviewed several times. Just when Green seemed ready to crack, he disappeared, never to be seen again. This happened just one day before the first Eucalyptus Lane break-in.

Case #2: *Arson and Murder.* The Bulky Woman Clothing store was near bankruptcy. Then one night, seven weeks ago, it went up in flames, killing a homeless man who had crawled inside for shelter. Traces of accelerant were discovered as was a hefty fire insurance policy. The owner, Jessica Grandee, had an alibi for the night of the fire, but she was still under suspicion. The nature of the work suggested to Chief Atkins that she had hired a professional. All attempts to track down the arsonist failed.

Case #3: *Kidnapping and Murder.* Holly Buckley, the daughter of Jason Buckley, was kidnapped after ballet class while waiting for the chauffeur. A ransom was paid and a week later Holly's body was found in the bush five miles out of town. Art Tyner, a former employee, had been seen loitering in the vicinity of the ransom's drop-off site, but there was never enough evidence to make an arrest.

"It's gotta be one of these cases," Chief Atkins theorized.

"Now, if I can just noggin out why my home was bashed in, I'm sure I'd know who to go after."

Whodunit? (1) Who sent the taunting note? (2) Why was the chief's house broken into three times? (3) What detail about the break-ins gave Chief Atkins the solution?

EVIDENCE *This case can be solved in one clue.*

Interview of the Postman
"All of Eucalyptus Lane is on my postie route. I was there all three times, Friday, Saturday, and Monday. I usually hit the Atkins's house at about 11:15 every working day. That's just a little while before those break-ins. Now I got a fair dinkum memory and eyes. But I don't recall seeing anything funny. No cars out of place, no one stalking around. Whoever it was must have been waiting till I turned the corner onto Currie."

Review of Videotape Evidence
At 11:41 on Monday morning, Chief Atkins's videocamera recorded the sound of the front door being forced open. It even caught the shuffle of shoes on the entry hall's floor. A shadow flitted across the frame, indicating someone had entered, but the intruder never stepped more than a few feet inside. Exactly twenty-one seconds after entering, he or she left the house and closed the door.

Review of Robbery File
A housekeeper reported hearing the Reverend Billy's end of this phone conversation: "It's the third time they came to question me. They know. I can't take the pressure. I have to confess, clear my conscience. ——That's all right for you to say. He's not after you. I'm going to tell Chief Atkins, make a clean breast of everything. ——Yes, everything. I don't care. ——No, I'm not going to jail. I'll disappear. Confess, then disappear. Wait! Someone's coming. I'll call you right back."

All this was overheard on Wednesday evening, one day before the Reverend's disappearance.

Review of Arson File
The Territorial Arson Squad identified the accelerant used to start the Bulky Woman fire. Chief Atkins determined that only one place in Adelaide, a cleaning supply company, carried this specific compound. On the day before the first break-in, the police department subpoenaed the company's records and narrowed the purchaser down to two possibilities, both men in their late twenties with criminal records in insurance fraud. No connection has been found between either man and Jessica Grandee. The cleaning supply company is located two blocks from the police chief's home.

Review of Kidnapping File
The only possible lead Chief Atkins has in this case is the ransom money, all of it in $100 and $50 bills. Several of the marked bills were passed in stores known to have been frequented by the suspected kidnapper, Art Tyner. One of the stores in question was the Bulky Woman, where Art shopped for clothes with his rather large girlfriend, Tina. A marked $50 bill was recovered from this location just one day prior to the Bulky Woman arson.

The Judge's Judgment Day

UIDO SENTINI ENTERED the downstairs drawing room. His mother glanced up and smiled. "That was very nice, taking up your father's breakfast."

"Ernesto did much of the serving. He knows how Papa likes it. I'm sure he thinks I must want something." The young playboy laughed. It was true, he did want something from his father. But he knew it would take more than a few breakfasts to make the stern judge part with the 60 million lire young Guido needed to pay off his debts.

The usual Vivaldi concerto poured down the stairs from the judge's second-floor office. "He's working," Yolanda Sentini sighed. Every day was like this, taking care of the estate and the servants while her husband, almost a stranger to her, was either off in the law courts of Naples or here at home, playing the same morning music and reviewing upcoming cases in his office. It was like being a widow, only without the freedom.

Down in the garden, Ernesto and the doctor both heard the Vivaldi. Reflexively, they looked up at Judge Sentini's curtained window and saw his seated silhouette at the desk. "A man of habits is easier to protect," Ernesto mumbled. He was the judge's bodyguard although he often felt like a maid. The government had hired him right after Judge Sentini sent a Mafia don to jail and received his first barrage of death threats.

Ernesto didn't consider his job a difficult one. They were in the Gulf of Naples, on an island with only a few private homes and no town to speak of. Unlike some of Ernesto's previous clients, the jurist followed his instructions to the letter. At night, Judge Sentini and his wife locked themselves into their suite with Ernesto's room right next door. On days when the judge worked at home, he locked himself into his office, as much for privacy as for safety. The alarm was always activated.

The gunshots came during a quiet stretch in the music—three bangs, one right after another, followed by a man's muffled cry of pain or alarm. Dr. Sentini, the judge's brother, glanced from the window to Ernesto, who was already running across the garden, through the hedge maze and toward the house.

It was less than 30 seconds later that Guido Sentini popped his head out of a second-story window. "The office door's locked," he shouted. Ernesto stopped running and was now fumbling for his own key. Guido saw this and shook his head. "No good. Papa left his key in the keyhole. We can't unlock it."

Ernesto's next actions seemed almost automatic. The gardener had left a pruning ladder up against a cherry tree. Ernesto grabbed it, flung it against the house and began to climb. When he reached the terrace window, the guard took out his semiautomatic and used the butt end to smash the glass. The sound of a siren screeched through the estate as he reached inside to find the latch and let himself in.

The alarm was still screaming when Ernesto unlocked the office door. Yolanda, Guido, and Dr. Sentini were waiting on the threshold. "He's dead," the terrified guard announced in disbelief.

Yolanda looked past him and saw her husband. The judge was face up on the carpet, three circles of blood emblazoned on his chest. Guido turned his mother away from the sight as Dr. Sentini rushed into the office.

"There's no one in the room," Ernesto stammered. "And no gun."

"Dead," the doctor confirmed as he knelt over his brother's body. "Guido, get your mother out of here. Ernesto, turn off that blasted alarm and call the police."

Guido and Ernesto did as they were told, returning to the office as soon as they could. The soothing strains of Vivaldi still filled the air. "Don't touch anything," Dr. Sentini said. "I have no idea how any assassin could get in, but we're locking this room until the police arrive."

They all watched as Ernesto turned the key and took up his post in front of the crime-scene door. He was still there a half-hour later when the Naples police docked at the jetty and raced up to the house, only to be faced with an impossible crime: a locked-room mystery that was to strike fear into the heart of every judge in Italy.

Whodunit?   (1) Who killed Judge Sentini?   (2) How did the killer get in and out of the locked office?   (3) What was the motive?

EVIDENCE   *This case can be solved in one clue.*

Autopsy Report

"Death was caused by three gunshot wounds, each approximately one centimeter in size. Entry points are the right chest wall, the left chest wall, and the sternum. No burn or gunpowder residue is present. Three .45-caliber automatic rounds have been recovered from the body. Death was probably instantaneous.

"A routine examination of body fluids reveals a high concentration of diazepam, a muscle relaxant often sold under the name Valium. Although not administered in a lethal dose, the drug nonetheless would be capable of producing severe muscle weakness, drowsiness, perhaps even a coma. An examination of the stomach contents suggests the diazepam was ingested fifteen minutes to a half-hour before death, probably in conjunction with food."

Search of the Murder Scene

"The body was discovered face up on the carpet, approximately halfway between the desk and the stereo system. The desk chair was found turned over on the floor. The carpet's pile flow indicates the decedent may have dragged himself or been dragged partly across the room. The stereo system was found still turned on, a tape of Vivaldi concerti in the cassette player.

"The suite is comprised of the office itself and an adjacent bathroom. Except for the terrace glass broken by the bodyguard, all windows were locked from the inside, as was the single door to the hallway.

"No firearm was found in the suite."

Chemical Analysis of the Victim's Breakfast

The remains of the decedent's breakfast tray were analyzed. Dissolved traces of diazepam were found in the coffee pot and in the coffee cup.

Search of the Medicine Cabinets

A half-empty container of Valium was discovered in the medicine cabinet of the master bedroom with a pharmaceutical label identifying it as the property of Yolanda Sentini. Signora Sentini admits to being under her brother-in-law's care for nervous distress. The master bedroom suite is locked only at night.

Alibis

Ernesto and Dr. Sentini were together in the far garden. Yolanda Sentini claimed to be in the drawing room drinking coffee—no corroboration. Guido Sentini was in his second-floor bedroom, adjacent to Judge Sentini's office—no corroboration. The gardener, cook, and maid were together in the basement kitchen having a late breakfast.

All suspects deny having yelled or cried out in the seconds following the gunshots.

The Masked Phantom

THE BOTAFOGO BAY district of Rio de Janeiro is not the best place for a woman walking alone at night. The main streets were still fairly safe at 12:30 A.M., but Carmen Neves had decided to take a shortcut down a lonely alley. It was her last, fatal mistake.

The witnesses all testified to hearing two gunshots. "I was walking down Rua Mariana," said Gomes Cavalho, a waiter who had just come off his shift. "A garbage truck was in the street. I thought it was backfiring. A few seconds later, I passed by the alley and looked inside. A woman was on the ground, and a man was kneeling over her. At the far end of the alley stood another woman. She looked like a passerby, like me."

The other passerby, Maria Gil, was an off-duty police officer. She had been on the parallel street, heard the shot, and seconds later glanced into the other end of the alley. "The kneeling man looked up from the body. He saw us, seemed a little dazed, and then he started shouting. 'He went that way. A masked bandit with a gun. Help!' The man pointed to a side alley a few feet ahead of him."

The witnesses both came to the kneeling man's aid. Maria pulled out her service revolver and gave chase into the narrow side alley. Gomes, more afraid for the female officer's safety than his own, followed. A minute later, they emerged back in the main alley, their faces troubled and wary. Maria aimed her weapon at the stranger, now standing over Carmen Neves's body. "The side alley is empty." She turned to Gomes Cavalho. "Call the police. I think we have our killer right here."

When the Rio homicide squad arrived, they agreed with Officer Gil. The side alley had turned out to be a dead end with only two doors opening onto it. One was the boarded-up door to an abandoned building. The other was the fire exit to Movie Palace, a door locked on the outside.

The suspect, Fernando Fernas, was an out-of-work carpenter. He was taken into custody and grilled for hours. "I'm innocent," he insisted and told his story once again. "I had just turned off the street into this alley. There was this woman walking ahead of me. She was about halfway through when this man jumped out. He was about average height with a beard and wearing a mask. I was still in the shadows. I stopped when I saw his gun. It looked like a robbery. But she wouldn't give him her purse. Then all of a sudden he shot her. Just like that—bang, bang. The killer started to come my way and then he saw me. That's when he turned and ran into the side alley. I know you say it's a dead end and there's no way he could have escaped. It's the truth. You have to believe me."

It was hard to believe. Fernando's story wouldn't have had any credibility at all, except for the missing gun. No gun was found—not on his person, not in the empty garbage cans, not in the scattered litter, nowhere in the entire neighborhood.

Turning their attention from Fernando to the side alley, the police returned to the scene and inspected the boarded-up door. Thick layers of dust and cobwebs gave mute testimony to the fact that no phantom had used that entrance.

Next on the list was the fire exit. Alvaro, a Movie Palace usher, listened to their questions, then shook his head. "Around 12:30? No. We're on a strict schedule. A show lets out at 12:10. Once the place is empty, we do our cleanup. Cashew boxes, drink cups. At 12:25, they start letting people in for the last show. That's when I take my post by the fire exit. This is a big auditorium and we used to have trouble with kids. The fire exit is hidden from view by a curtain. Kids used to push open the door and let their friends sneak in. That's why I'm there. I stand on the inside of that door from the time they let people in until the movie's almost over. Then it's my turn for a break."

The police showed the usher's testimony to Fernando. "There's no way your masked killer could disappear. Come clean, Fernando. What did you do with the gun?" But Fernando protested his innocence and they had to let him go. "Don't leave town," the chief of detectives warned.

It was two nights later when the phantom struck again. At 12:20 A.M., another foolish pedestrian took a shortcut. This woman was luckier than the first. She had walked only ten feet into the alley when a masked man of average height popped out from the side alley, his gun drawn. But the would-be robber had miscalculated the distance to his victim. He was far enough away so that the woman didn't feel compelled to obey. The masked man motioned with his gun. "Come here," he growled. And the woman screamed.

Within seconds, a passerby came to her aid. Together they watched as the gunman fled, disappearing down the same side alley. Just as before, the passerby gave chase. And just as before, the phantom vanished.

"Perhaps Fernando was telling the truth," said the chief of detectives begrudgingly. "Our killer must know some way out of the dead-end alley. Let's just hope we catch him before he strikes again."

Whodunit? (1) Who killed Carmen Neves? (2) How did the killer make his two escapes? (3) What were the motives for the attacks?

EVIDENCE *This case can be solved in two clues.*

Inspection of the Fire Door
Even though the Movie Palace's fire door had been thoroughly inspected after the first crime, the chief ordered a second inspection. A tacky, gluelike residue was found on the latch and the adjoining few inches above and below it, indicating that the mechanism on the door's inside edge had been taped open. The officer in charge swears that no such residue had been there during his first inspection.

Search of the Garbage Dump
A day after the second attack, a ten-year-old girl was scavenging through the South Zone's main garbage dump and found a loaded .45-caliber revolver. She sold it to an off-duty security guard who brought the weapon in to Rio's central police department. A ballistics test showed that this gun had fired the bullet that killed Carmen Neves.

Alibis for Second Attack, 12:20 A.M.
- Fernando Fernas claims to have been at home asleep. No witnesses.
- Gomes Cavalho had just gotten off work and decided to see a movie. He claims to have been inside the Movie Palace lobby, waiting in line to be let into the theater. Several witnesses tentatively identify him, but no one is absolutely sure.
- Maria Gil was on solo foot patrol in the general vicinity. Local shopkeepers recall seeing her but aren't positive about the time.
- Alvaro was in the theater auditorium, cleaning up litter and tying up garbage bags. His activities were witnessed by two other ushers.
- Raul Filho was in police custody, booked on a charge of assault and burglary of an English tourist in the Ipanema district.

None of the suspects have any known connection to the victim.

Search of Neighborhood Streets
In the aftermath of the killer's second appearance, a squadron of officers fanned out through the neighborhood, interviewing passersby and looking for leads. In the trash can of a public men's room, an officer spotted a black mask. Under the mask was a false beard, a man's wig, and a .22-caliber starter's pistol. Fernando Fernas and the witnesses from the second attack identified the mask as belonging to the phantom. All three witnesses also testified that the killer had been bearded, with hair similar in style to the wig.

Search of the Abandoned Building
Several squatters, including Raul Filho, a burglar with four prior convictions, were discovered to be living in the boarded-up building across the side alley from the Movie Palace. At the time of the murder, Raul claims to have been strolling along Ipanema Beach. His common-law wife, Isabel, says she was with him at the time.

Suicide Incorporated

NEW YORK IS a high-pressure town and being CEO of Yungun Best Advertising was a high-pressure job. The agency's founder, George Yungun, had died of a massive coronary at the age of fifty-three. His replacement, Keith Best, was barely on the job a week when he followed in his partner's footsteps. A suicide, or so it seemed at first.

It was on a Monday morning when Bonny Lou discovered the body. Keith Best's longtime assistant and occasional fiancée, Bonny Lou arrived at the Madison Avenue offices early that day, getting off the elevator on the executive floor and putting on coffee. As the percolator hummed, she glanced into Keith's office and immediately noticed something different. Her boss was dangling from the room's tasteful chandelier, supported only by a stylishly strong necktie. A suicide note on his desk cited the usual litany of depression and regret.

By that evening, New York's finest had labeled it murder. Keith's suicide note did not quite match his handwriting, and a severe contusion on the crown of his head showed that he'd been knocked unconscious before being strung up.

As shocking as the murder was, it took a backseat to the nastier world of office politics. The wrangling for the job of CEO had been intense before Keith Best's promotion. After his death it became doubly intense. The top two contenders for the vacant position were the creative director, Robert Godenov, and the chief financial officer, Betina Anderson. Both were in their midthirties and ruthlessly ambitious.

Two days before the board of directors was scheduled to choose, Herb Anderson, Betina's father, was at his post on the night desk in the Yungun Best lobby. At 8:06 P.M., his intercom buzzed. Someone was calling from the executive floor. Right away Herb recognized the voice. "Mr. Godenov? Hello? What's wrong? You sound . . ."

"Herb, call an ambulance! 911! I've been poisoned. Blast her sneaky, interfering . . . Hurry, man! It's an emergency!"

Less than a minute after arriving on the executive floor, the paramedics discovered Robert Godenov in the founding chairman's office, crumpled in front of George Yungun's massive desk. He had died just moments earlier. A preliminary autopsy confirmed that death had been caused by potassium cyanide. A hundred feet away, in Robert Godenov's office, lay a suicide note. But once again, the police weren't buying suicide.

Days later, Betina Anderson was arrested on two counts of first-degree murder. Patty Yungun, the late founder's daughter, was appointed as acting CEO.

In the prosecution's opening statement, the district attorney outlined three pieces of evidence: two forged suicide notes and a letter to Robert Godenov, luring him to a secret meeting that evening at eight.

"Betina Anderson will tell you that she was at home at the time, alone. Her father, the office security guard, will show you the sign-in log and tell you that his daughter never returned to the building. Well, who can blame a father for protecting his child? But this time, Ms. Anderson left us some clues.

"First," the district attorney held up an evidence bag, "a typed letter found in Mr. Godenov's bottom drawer in which Ms. Anderson set up their last fatal appointment. And then, even more damning . . ." A second evidence bag. "This so-called suicide note, written on the same paper and with the same pen as Keith Best's forged suicide note. It all fits together. Betina Anderson lured Robert Godenov back to the office, poisoned his coffee with cyanide, then made her escape, planting a suicide note on his desk.

"But Robert Godenov did not die as quickly as he was supposed to. His recorded call down to the security desk reveals a diabolical plot engineered by a 'sneaky, interfering' woman, the victim's own words. Ladies and gentlemen, that woman is Betina Anderson."

Whodunit? (1) Who killed Keith Best? (2) Who killed Robert Godenov? (3) How did Robert Godenov ingest the cyanide?

EVIDENCE   *This case can be solved in two clues.*

Holographic Expert
"The Keith Best suicide note is the better of the two forgeries and resembles Mr. Best's handwriting in most of the details. The second example, the Godenov suicide note, was definitely written by the same person. There are aspects of this note that mirror Mr. Godenov's hand. Other aspects clearly indicate Ms. Anderson's writing."

The Godenov suicide note:

"To Whom It May Concern,

The police will soon discover the truth, that I murdered Keith. I wanted so desperately to become CEO. I can no longer live with the guilt and I would rather die than face the inevitable exposure and shame. I ask my friends and the Best family to forgive me." (*unsigned*)

Appointment Letter
This typewritten letter was found in a plain, sealed envelope in Robert Godenov's bottom-right drawer.

"We've both been promised things by Yungun Best and we've both been passed over and treated shabbily. Suddenly, we're in a good position and (who knows?) there may be some advantage in combining forces. Meet me tonight. Eight. In my office. I don't have to tell you to keep this secret. (*signed*) B."

Cleaning Lady's Testimony
"I was on the executive floor a few minutes before eight, taking a break. I made myself a cup of coffee and was searching for some sweetener. They were all out of saccharine, but some of them keep a few packets hidden away. Anyway, I had just found a partly used packet somewhere and was about to use it when I heard the elevator. I didn't want anyone to see me goofing off; so, I left everything on the counter, then took my mop and pail and hit the stairs to the next floor. As I walked up, I could hear Mr. Godenov's voice, kind of mumbling. I know him 'cause he sometimes works late. I don't know if he

was talking to himself or someone else. I didn't hear anyone else."

Paramedic on the Scene

"We found Mr. Godenov's body in Mr. Yungun's old office. Several drawers were open and their contents scattered. It looked like Mr. Godenov had been looking for something. As I was trying to revive him, I noticed an ampoule of amyl nitrite in his hand. I found out later that the late Mr. Yungun had a heart condition and kept amyl nitrite in the office just in case he had an attack. Now, amyl nitrite is a kind of low-level antidote for cyanide. Mr. Godenov must have known he'd been poisoned. He also knew the antidote, and was trying to inhale some when he died."

Officer on the Scene

"On the coffee counter, I found two mugs of coffee, both relatively hot. One was black, unsweetened. No prints. The other was about half full. Black, unsweetened, mixed with potassium cyanide. Victim's prints on the cup. Also on the counter was a coffee stirrer. Wet. Plus an open jar of instant coffee. The other things, sugar packets and stuff; none of it looked like it had been touched. The trash can was fairly full. Leftovers from the work day.

"I checked the security log downstairs in the lobby. It showed Mr. Godenov signing in at 7:55. No other sign-ins."

Death of the Salesmen

Barry Naybors was busy raking up leaves when he heard the scream. It was coming from the thick patch of trees behind his house. By the time Barry threw down his rake and ran up the wooded path, the piercing shriek had stopped. Little Nellie Shell stood frozen in the middle of the path, ready to scream again. "Nellie, what's the matter?"

The 11-year-old pointed. A blood-stained shirt hung from a low branch, blocking the path. Barry looked past the shirt and saw what had made Nellie scream. It was a man staring blankly up at them from the bottom of a ravine. They were close enough to make an identification. The thick, black-frame glasses, the colorful tattoo on the left forearm, the balding head. "It's Mr. Chirac," Nellie wailed. "See the knife?" Barry saw. A kitchen steak knife protruded gruesomely from a gash in Joël Chirac's bare chest.

Fifteen minutes later, the Toronto police arrived at Barry Naybors's house. "I took Nellie home," the long-haul trucker explained as he led the troopers to the site. "She's been told a hundred times not to use the woods as a shortcut to school. But you know kids. The bloody shirt is . . ." Barry paused and looked around. "It's gone."

Not only was the shirt gone, but so was the body. A trooper lowered himself into the ravine and began to inspect the flattened branches. "Are you sure you really saw . . ." Then his eyes fell on the bloody steak knife.

At the local hospital, Annette Chirac was nearing the end of her shift. Annette was French Canadian, like her husband of two years. Both were known to speak passable English. "Joël works for a drug company," the petite nurse said. "He left this morning on one of his sales trips. Is anything wrong?"

The senior trooper gently explained the situation. "My poor, foolish . . ." Annette wrung her hands. "I told him to take those threats seriously."

"Threats?" The trooper perked up. "What threats?"

Back at home, Annette showed them a trio of letters, all promising Joël Chirac that he would soon die. "The first came last month. Once, when he was on the road, I got a phone call.

A man whispering—same sort of thing. There didn't seem to be any motive; so, Joël never took them seriously."

The police launched an intensive investigation. The only clue, a bloody fingerprint on the knife, was put through the department's AFIS computer and miraculously came up with a match. Nathaniel Sims, a sales representative for a rival drug company, had his prints on file, the result of a traffic arrest years earlier. Sims lived 170 kilometers away and had no known association with Joël Chirac.

Sims was brought in for questioning. He seemed shy and harmless and claimed to have no idea how his prints could have gotten on the knife. The police couldn't help noticing the tissue paper stuffed up one nostril. "I've been having a lot of nosebleeds lately," the timid suspect explained. "It's just nerves."

The next day, they placed Sims in a lineup, hoping Chirac's wife could identify him. As Annette Chirac studied the faces, her eyes kept returning to Sims. Suddenly she was nervous. Several times Annette seemed about to speak, but never did. And she never made an identification.

Just a few hours after the lineup, the police had their evidence. The blood on the weapon matched Sims's blood type. Also, a check of phone records showed a call from the Sims house to Chirac's on the same day Annette received the phone threat.

When the police arrived with an arrest warrant, Betty Sims invited them in. "Nathaniel just left. Moose season starts tomorrow. He never misses it, except when he's on some sales trip. He camps out the night before, just to get an early start. I don't know exactly where."

An all-points-bulletin described Nathaniel Sims's car. Shortly after dawn, a Mountie spotted the tan Pontiac in a roadside turnout. He trudged up the nearest path and soon found his man at a campsite. Nathaniel Sims was still half-zipped into his sleeping bag, held in place by a steak knife that looked suspiciously like the knife used on Joël Chirac. Dead.

Whodunit? (1) What happened to Joël Chirac? (2) Who killed Nathaniel Sims? (3) What clue connects the killer to the crime?

EVIDENCE   *This case can be solved in one clue.*

Interviews and Alibis

Barry Naybors had just returned from a long haul into the hinterlands of New Brunswick. "Been driving for two days. I pulled my rig into the dock about six this morning, then went home to bed." Naybors was asked about his friendship with Annette Chirac. "Her husband was on the road a lot. When I was home, she used to come over and talk." He scraped the caked dirt out from under his fingernails. "I guess she was pretty lonely."

The police questioned Annette Chirac at the hospital, just as she was leaving work. "After I got home from the lineup, I went right to bed. I got up at eleven and arrived here at midnight when my shift began." Annette seemed nervous. Her hands fumbled with the buttons on the right side of her oversized red parka as she buttoned it up.

Betty Sims described her evening. "Nathaniel packed up the Pontiac and left around eight. I kissed him good-bye at the curb. There was another car. It started up and drove off a few seconds after Nathaniel. I didn't see what type or color." The widow fingered the keys of her own car, a white Toyota. "I didn't mention this last night because it didn't seem important."

Information about Victims

Nathaniel Sims was born into a French-English family in Montréal and is survived by his wife of eleven years, two sons, and his mother. For the past ten years, Sims worked for Maxxon Drugs, and his sales territory encompassed a 250-kilometer radius of Toronto.

Joël Chirac was an orphan raised in Québec, Québec, by relatives now deceased. According to Annette, they met in Toronto two and a half years ago. Shortly thereafter, Joël acquired his sales job at Walling Pharmaceutical. The police are currently checking out Chirac's previous job history.

While Joël Chirac was a bold, flashy dresser, Nathaniel Sims was conservative in taste. Both were about the same age, and their territories covered approximately the same area.

Wills and Insurance

Shortly after their husbands' deaths, Annette Chirac and Betty Sims filed insurance claims. Since their husbands both died from acts of violence, both widows were entitled to double indemnity, double the normal payoff. The policies were part of the benefits package provided by the men's employers and would pay out $500,000 apiece. Both widows were the sole beneficiaries.

Campsite Investigation

The scene of Nathaniel Sims's murder is 35 kilometers from the Sims residence and 150 kilometers from the Chirac residence. An inspection of the campfire ashes revealed the charred remains of a small, heavy green jacket. No other outerwear was discovered at the site, leading to the assumption that the killer burned the deceased's coat.

The deceased was clean-shaven with an old scar on his left forearm. A preliminary examination indicated cause of death to have been a single stab wound to the heart. The deceased's sleeping bag and the surrounding few feet were saturated with blood. A toupee was found among the deceased's possessions. Mrs. Sims and various neighbors confirmed the fact that, for the past ten years at least, the deceased was in the habit of wearing a hairpiece.

Search for Joël Chirac's Car

Annette Chirac testified that her husband drove off on a business trip the morning of his murder. Mme. Chirac described his car as a late-model tan Pontiac but was unable to supply police with the license number. An inspection of the deceased's papers have failed to turn up registration or ownership papers, and to date, no trace of the car has been found.

Analysis of Evidence

Stories are in alphabetical order.

Attack of the Werewolf

The slashed throat, the presence of wolves, and the absence of human footprints start the local peasantry whispering about werewolves. But there are mysteries here that can't be blamed on the supernatural. For instance, why was the blood mopped up from the cottage floor? Why was the body moved to the river? What is Factor VIII? And why did someone mutilate the already dead corpse?

The list of the American's possessions is notable not only for what it contained but for what it didn't contain. The absence of one item from the cottage points directly to a strong motive.

Only Dr. Ionescu has an alibi for the fifteen minutes prior to the body's discovery. On the other hand, Ionescu is the only suspect without an alibi from 10:30 to 11:00.

The Baffling Break-ins

Here are the facts we have to go on. The break-ins occurred on Friday, Saturday, and Monday between 11:30 and noon, shortly after the mail delivery. Nothing was stolen or disturbed, and on the last occasion the intruder did not take more than a few steps inside. Since this was the intruder's last foray into the house, we can probably assume that the intruder accomplished his or her mission with this final, minimal entry.

The connection between Art Tyner, the suspected kidnapper, and the Bulky Woman store, the site of the arson, appears tenuous. His girlfriend, Tina, was "big-boned" and likely to have shopped at this store. The fact that the cleaning supply company that was the source of the accelerant used for arson is only two blocks from the chief's home also appears coincidental.

The Bee All and End All

Four points seem worthy of investigation: honey, the puncture marks, time, and the groundskeeper.

First off, the honey. Why would Beatrice risk exposure by doing something so risky as coating the hammock bottom with honey? The bee-sting story would have been almost as convincing without a lot of bees humming around.

Next comes the puzzle of the double puncture wounds. Had the first one been a mistake, a slip of the hand? It's possible. But there just might be another explanation.

The third question, time. Would Beatrice have had enough time after the supposed bee sting to wipe off the syringe and dispose of it in the garden hose?

And finally, there's the groundskeeper. If he's telling the truth, then the syringe had not been shoved up the hose until after Beatrice left to accompany her uncle to the hospital. This points to a frame-up by one of the other cousins. The lack of fingerprints on the syringe also points to this. Wiped-off prints mean the killer was expecting the weapon to be found, something Bea would not have planned on.

The Day of the Dead

On the day before the murder, Hugo made a good point. Plenty of people, men and women, could have motives for killing Maria's late husband.

The location and date of Maria's murder, replicating those of her husband's death, are too great to be labeled a coincidence. Also, the fact that the footbridge railing had been sawed through makes this murder seem well planned.

The two notes were either both written by the killer or by Maria herself. Likewise, the mannequin had either been placed at the window by the killer or by Maria. The most logical reason would be to provide an alibi or to disguise the time of death.

As for Maria, several facts seem significant. The weekend party mirroring the party from a year ago, the employment of private investigators, the torn-off button—all these point to the hostess's involvement in some secret plan.

On close examination, Maria's frugal but organized system of entertaining may provide a pivotal clue to her killer's identity.

Death of a Dummy

Due to lack of an obvious motive, the best approach might be to concentrate on the physical evidence first.

The poison took effect in one to three minutes, logically placing the victim in the kitchen at the time of ingestion. A granule was found in his teeth, indicating that the poison had not been dissolved in a liquid. Since no cyanide was discovered in any foodstuffs, it's probable that the victim ate the only tainted item. This eliminates the identical minipastries, since the killer had no way of knowing which one the victim would filch. The presence of cyanide traces on the dish towel leads to the assumption that either the killer or victim wiped his hands on the towel after touching the poison.

The sticky cards present an interesting problem. How did the cards get sticky?

Death of the Salesmen

The two victims had several things in common. They were about the same age, originally from Québec and employed as pharmaceutical sales reps. Both drove similar cars and were killed with similar knives. Both were insured with double-indemnity policies, although this can be explained by the fact that they worked for companies with similar benefits packages.

The bloody fingerprints on the knife and the phone call point to some connection between Sims and Chirac. But while Sims's background seems fairly straightforward, Chirac's personal history only seems to date back two and a half years.

The green jacket remnants found in the ashes are puzzling, since only a rather foolish hunter would dress in green. Red and orange tend to be the hunter's colors of choice.

One other oddity. Why would a killer leave Joël Chirac's shirt on a branch blocking the path? Perhaps the body was meant to be found by the schoolgirl who regularly took that shortcut.

Death Takes a Ski Weekend

The footprints tell us that Belle walked out to the caretaker's cottage, perhaps for a romantic rendezvous. There she met someone who accompanied her back to the chalet, where she apparently changed both her wig and her clothes.

There are two discrepancies in the physical evidence. (1) Gretel testified that Belle's hand was cold. Half an hour later, the police found the victim still warm. (2) When the witnesses first saw them, both wig stands were empty. On the police's arrival, however, the shorter-styled wig was back on its stand. Clearly, someone had been on the murder scene between the discovery of the body and the arrival of the police.

The murder seems to have happened within a 10-minute time frame during which everyone had an ironclad alibi. This suggests that the murder may not have occurred within that limited time.

The Judge's Judgment Day

Everyone in the house had access to the diazepam. The three suspects who could have most easily placed it in the judge's coffee are Yolanda, who brewed it; Ernesto, who arranged the breakfast tray; and Guido, who poured the judge's first cup.

The huge, frightening puzzle of the murder—how an unseen killer could get in, get out, and dispose of his gun without being seen or triggering the alarm—can be broken down into a series of smaller puzzles.

The first is the man's muffled cry heard just after the gunshots. It had to come either from Guido or from the judge himself. Guido denies having made any such sound, and the autopsy indicates that the judge died almost instantly.

The next puzzle involves the dragged body. If the judge dragged himself, then his death was not instantaneous. If, on the other hand, the killer dragged him, he or she must have had a good reason for taking valuable time to do this.

The presence of diazepam in the judge's system brings up the third puzzle. Why? If the killer just wanted to kill, why didn't he or she use a more effective poison? It would have been much less risky than a shooting. Or why not just shoot the judge without the poison? Why were both methods necessary?

The Marquis de Sade's Locked Room

Since the Napoléon letter is still missing and there seems to be no other reason to kill Professor Petit, we can assume that possession of the letter is the motive behind the murder.

The absence of luggage and the lack of personal effects in the room seem puzzling, even when taking into account that the victim was on the lam and traveling light. The most logical explanation is that someone other than the professor rented the room.

But the crux of this case lies in how *anyone* could have removed the Napoléon letter from the inner room. Once this mystery is fathomed, we'll probably have all the answers we need.

The professor certainly seems implicated. His free-spending ways on Friday night, his flight to a hotel on Sunday, and his calling card left on the table all point to this. And yet, . . . if Professor Petit had been planning to steal the letter, why did he bother to tell the de Sade family about its existence? That seems counterproductive.

The bank guard cannot be completely ruled out as an accomplice, although he does have an alibi for the time of the professor's murder.

The Masked Phantom

The presence of the garbage truck on Rua Mariana at the time of the first attack suggests a simple way for the killer to dispose of the first gun. Simply toss it into a garbage bag or into the truck itself. This is supported by the discovery of the gun days later in a garbage dump.

The dust and cobwebs on the boarded-up door rule out the abandoned building as a means of escape, and that leaves the movie theater as the only plausible route. The tape residue on the latch reveals that the fire door had been used for the second escape. The phantom probably sneaked in while the ushers were cleaning and hid behind the curtain until the auditorium started filling up. But to do this, the killer had to be aware of the theater's schedule.

For the first escape to work, however, (a) the police had to be wrong about the lack of tape residue and (b) Alvaro the usher had to be involved. Either that, or Fernando lied about the killer running into the side alley. The possibility also exists that Fernando was simply mistaken. Perhaps he'd been so preoccupied with the murdered woman that he didn't really see the masked killer leave.

The most puzzling puzzle, however, may be the disguise. If the police had found the gun on the killer after the first attack, that would have been an incriminating piece of evidence. That's why the killer got rid of it. But the disguise would have been just as incriminating. So, why didn't the killer dispose of the disguise at the same time?

River of No Return

There appear to be only two possible motives: one, inheritance, since his wife, Sophia profited from Jan's death, or two, fraud. Infant Philanthropies could be a concoction of Margo's or of the Westins', who run an English charity with a similar name.

There is one glaring discrepancy in testimony. Sophia testified that Jan did not leave the hotel gates between 2 P.M. and 5 P.M. But the concierge gave Jan a hiking map at 2:30 and several people saw him leave.

Special attention should be paid to Gordon Armgaard. Although the Dutchman said on Thursday that he had to drive to Lisbon to catch a flight, a red Renault, similar to his rental car, was seen hidden behind rocks between Thursday and Saturday. This was only a kilometer or so from the spot where the body was eventually found.

One last oddity. Why was Jan deWys wearing sunglasses on a rainy afternoon?

Suicide Incorporated

A few confusing points. For instance, Godenov seemed to know how he'd been poisoned and what the antidote was, things the average citizen wouldn't know. And the letter setting up the appointment: According to police, it was found in a bottom drawer, in a blank, *sealed* envelope. Godenov's last recorded words also seem a little odd. He refers to the woman as conniving and sneaky, hardly a damning accusation from a man facing death.

Since both forged suicide notes were written by the same person, we can assume that there is only one killer.

As for the coffee, the full cup had probably been poured by the cleaning lady and therefore cannot be taken as evidence of the killer's presence. The lack of prints on the mug could simply mean that the cleaning lady was wearing rubber gloves.

Twice Terminated

The presence of medicine packaging in the garbage is quite significant when linked to the absence of both the bottle and safety seal. Combined with the victim's cold, this points to the liquid medicine as the most likely source of the strychnine. The origin of the tainted medicine is unknown.

Three other facts seem worth noting: The broken locks on Dinsmore's suitcases indicate that the killer may have been looking for something. The horizontal crease on the leather band shows that the watch had been worn by someone with a smaller wrist. The third fact remains unexplained. Why would an expensive watch be sixty-five minutes off the correct time?

But the most puzzling mystery is this: Why would a man undergoing painful symptoms suffer silently instead of using the telephone to seek help?

Solutions

Stories are in alphabetical order.

Attack of the Werewolf

(1) Dr. Ionescu. (2) To retrieve the incriminating diary. (3) The doctor realized that Tim's hemophilia would give him an alibi, if no one else discovered it.

The mystery unraveled when the militia determined that Factor VIII is a blood protein used by hemophiliacs. This was what Tim shared with his maternal grandfather: blood that would not clot. The killer obviously wanted to hide this fact. That was why he mopped up the blood, then went to all the trouble of transporting the corpse to the river and slashing the veins.

Dr. Ionescu had been Werner Havardi's partner in crime, engineering the theft of Communist party funds. When Werner began to be plagued by his conscience and seemed on the verge of confessing, Ionescu felt he had no option but murder. The doctor got away with this crime, too, until Werner's diary made an unexpected appearance in Tim's hands. The odds were good that Werner had left a record of his sins.

After leaving the tavern, Dr. Ionescu went to the Havardi cottage and tried to retrieve the diary. Tim became suspicious and Ionescu was once again forced into murder. The rain hadn't yet started, thereby accounting for the lack of footprints.

Later on, when he and the mayor examined the body, Ionescu was delighted to find his victim's blood still liquid, leading everyone to assume the murder had just been committed. Suddenly he had an alibi. The only challenge remaining was to keep everyone else from discovering Tim's hemophilia.

During the night, the doctor returned to the unlocked cottage. He dragged the body to the waterfall, trying to get rid of as much blood as possible. If there was no sign of Tim's unusual blood, the police would not think of sending off samples for testing. His one mistake was not checking Tim's toiletries for an emergency supply of Factor VIII.

The Baffling Break-ins

(1) The Reverend Billy's accomplice.   (2) Billy mailed in a confession. His accomplice broke in to recover it.   (3) Break-ins occurred only after mail deliveries.

Eventually, the answer dawned on Chief Atkins. The intruder had been after a piece of mail. That's why the break-ins happened when they did and why his house was not broken into on Sunday.

Armed with this theory, Chief Atkins pieced together a plausible scenario. On Wednesday night, the last night before his disappearance, the Reverend Billy Green telephoned his partner in the church robbery. Green revealed his determination to mail his complete confession to Chief Atkins's home. He then planned to run away. To escape arrest, the accomplice knew he had to intercept the letter before Chief Atkins got his hands on it.

The earliest possible day for the letter's arrival was Friday. For three days, the accomplice lay in wait, watching for the Eucalyptus Lane mail delivery. Each day, after the postman vanished around the corner of Currie Street, the accomplice broke into the house, staying just long enough to check the freshly delivered mail. On Monday morning, the Reverend's letter finally arrived and the accomplice retrieved it from the entryway floor.

Postscript: The Reverend Billy Green was apprehended two months later in Alice Springs. He readily confessed and named his accomplice, the Second Baptist Church's choir director.

The Bee All and End All

(1) Ace Purdy. (2) With formic acid in a syringe. (3) At the hospital as Lord Purdy was recovering from a bee sting.

There is only one theory that adequately reconciles the honey, the two punctures, and the groundskeeper's testimony.

The killer first tried the natural method, spreading honey on the hammock bottom and hoping Lord Purdy would get stung. He did get stung and it was merely coincidence that Beatrice happened to be with him.

Later, in the hospital, when Lord Purdy refused to die, the killer switched to Plan B. Left alone at the old man's bedside, the killer pulled out a syringe previously stolen from Beatrice's medical bag and injected him, trusting that the second puncture site would simply blend in with the first.

The murder might have gone undetected, but the family doctor grew suspicious and ordered an autopsy. Bea became the most logical person to take the fall. After all, she was the one who'd been at the hammock. And it was her syringe. On returning to the estate, the killer hid her syringe in a spot where it was bound to be discovered.

According to this, only one of the cousins could be guilty. Only Ace had both gone to the hospital and returned to the estate before the syringe was found.

The Day of the Dead

(1) Hugo.   (2) Self-defense and to prevent arrest; either is acceptable.   (3) The frugal Maria did not buy fish for Hugo's Saturday dinner, expecting him to be dead by then.

Exactly one year earlier, fate caught up with Pepe Monteneras. Hugo had discovered that his wife, Yolanda, had been having an affair with the over-sexed Pepe. The jealous husband waylaid the drunken Pepe on the footbridge, pushing him to his death.

From the very beginning, Maria suspected murder. But it was a few weeks later, when she found the strange torn-off button wedged in a rock where her husband had fallen, that she hired her private eyes. It took months of investigation, but they finally traced the button to a hand-made jacket Hugo had bought six years before in Acapulco.

Maria had her killer. And he had to pay for his crime in the same way Pepe paid. On the anniversary of Pepe's death, she would lure Hugo to the bridge, then push him through the carefully sawed railing. The mannequin would provide Maria with an alibi. She would sneak back into the cottage by 1:30 at the latest. Everyone would swear she had been in there, working on her book.

But Maria's plan backfired. Hugo was suspicious. As soon as she attacked, he overpowered her, propelling her into the dry riverbed instead.

Maria's lifelong habits of thrift came to her aid after death. She had not expected Hugo to be alive to eat Saturday's dinner. So, there was no reason to buy a good piece of fish that would just go uneaten.

Death of a Dummy

(1) Paterno, Gleason's best friend.   (2) By poisoning the cherry on top of the cake.   (3) The sticky cards on the table.

Years ago, Paterno (born Yuri Patrenko) was planted in the CIA. It was arranged for him to have a fellow KGB mole as his examining physician. In this way, Paterno's telltale vaccination scars and dental work went unreported.

Though the Cold War was over, Paterno still worked for Russia. Gleason, who had seen Paterno half-naked on various beaches, was about to be briefed on the details of such marks and would have connected this information to his friend.

Paterno brought the cyanide, knowing that Gleason was famous for picking at food, especially desserts. When Paterno saw the candied cherry, he knew Gleason wouldn't be able to resist. During his turn as dummy, Paterno filled the pitted fruit with several grains of poison, then replaced it on the marshmallow icing. Paterno's hands were now sticky from the cherry and the icing, but there was no water to wash his fingers. He certainly couldn't lick them. So, he wiped them off as best he could on a dish towel.

When Gleason filched the cherry during his last kitchen visit, he smoothed over the icing with his fingers, leaving no trace of the cherry, then licked his fingers clean.

During their last full hand, Paterno's sticky hands gummed up the cards, leading Gleason to break out a new deck. Paterno was shuffling this new deck when Gleason collapsed. No one else had touched the deck and yet it also proved to be sticky, just like the old one.

The CIA pieced together this scenario and removed Agent Paterno from Prague. His name soon disappeared from their list of active agents.

Death of the Salesmen

(1) Joël Chirac and Nathaniel Sims were the same person. (2) Annette Chirac. (3) The man's hunting jacket, which Annette was wearing after the murder.

Two and a half years ago, on a business trip, Nathaniel met Annette. At the time, Nathaniel's toupee was being restyled, and he wasn't wearing his contact lenses. Being a married man, Nathaniel gave Annette a false name, Joël Chirac, just to be safe.

Nathaniel fell in love. But he had no intention of divorcing Betty and losing his sons. So, he created a second life. As Joël Chirac, he found work with a rival drug company. Being his own competition, Nathaniel could manage both jobs, spending half his time with Betty and the other half with Annette, dressing differently, wearing his toupee and covering up his scar with a temporary tattoo. The only thing that remained constant was his tan Pontiac.

But the double life grew exhausting. Nathaniel's best way out was to fake Joël's death, leaving Annette with a rich settlement. He sent the death threats and made the whispering phone call. Using his nosebleed to supply the blood, Nathaniel then set the scene, knowing the schoolgirl would discover his "corpse" and run off for help.

Nathaniel's troubles began when the police traced his fingerprints. They escalated when Annette recognized him in the lineup. She waited for him outside the police station, then tailed him home. A short time later, when Nathaniel drove off on his hunting trip, she followed.

Annette stabbed him with a second steak knife from her kitchen and blood spurted all over her green jacket. It would have been too dangerous to drive the 150 kilometers home with a bloody jacket. So, Annette burned her own jacket in the campfire and took Nathaniel's, driving to work just in time for her shift.

The police deduced that a hunter would not be wearing a green jacket and that the oversized red jacket Annette wore had the buttons on the right, an indication that it was a man's style.

Death Takes a Ski Weekend

(1) Boris Stuttgart, her husband.   (2) He laid out Paulina's body with the wig, killing Belle later.   (3) Jealousy over Belle's infidelity.

Belle Stuttgart and Hansel Aroma had been having an affair. Boris discovered this and carefully bided his time, waiting for just the right opportunity. That opportunity came with Paulina's heart attack. The fact that the women were fairly similar in build and age gave him his inspiration.

Boris forged a love note from Hansel, knowing that Belle would rush off at six o'clock to the caretaker's cottage. He also knew that Hansel's conference call would keep the lovers from bumping into each other during that critical period.

Before going to the lounge, Boris used the terrace to move Paulina's body from one guest room to the other, covering up her gym outfit with the silk robe and one of Belle's distinctive wigs. When he brought the two witnesses back to his room, they naturally assumed this "strangled" corpse was Belle's.

While Boris was supposedly off by himself mourning, he walked out to the cottage, where he surprised his wife who was still waiting for Hansel. Belle tried to cover up her guilt and willingly accompanied him back to their bedroom. Belle was astonished by the sight of the blond corpse and Boris seized his chance, strangling her from behind. During Belle's brief struggle, the note fell from her pocket.

Then came the cleanup. He undressed his wife. Then he removed the robe and wig from the cold corpse, placing them on the fresh corpse and arranging the body in the same position. Finally, he carried Paulina's corpse back across the terrace to the other guest room. Everyone would believe that Belle was dead a good fifteen minutes before she actually was, thereby giving Boris his alibi.

The Judge's Judgment Day

(1) Ernesto, the bodyguard. (2) The gunshot sounds were on the Vivaldi tape. Ernesto shot the drugged judge before letting anyone into the room. (3) A paid Mafia assassination.

The Mafia had to make an example of Judge Sentini. A simple poisoning or a simple shooting would not inspire half the fear that an impossible, phantom murder would. Ernesto was paid a lot of money to arrange it, and all he needed from his employers was a duplicate of the judge's favorite Vivaldi tape, one with the sound of three gunshots placed strategically in the middle section.

Ernesto had keys to the office. It was very easy for him to enter one evening and replace the judge's morning tape with the "gunshot" one. The next morning, while preparing the breakfast tray, Ernesto drugged the coffee pot, then left to find himself an alibi witness in the garden.

As always, the judge followed Ernesto's instructions, locking the door and leaving the key in the lock. He drank his coffee and turned on his music, all part of his unvarying routine. When the gunshots sounded on the tape, Judge Sentini was already partly paralyzed from the diazepam. He cried out in alarm and got up to check the stereo. Then he collapsed, dragging himself partway across the floor.

When Ernesto broke the terrace window, he counted on the alarm to cover up the sound of the real murder. He screwed a silencer onto the muzzle of his semiautomatic, killed his boss, then unlocked the door to admit the rest of the household.

The assassin knew it would take at least thirty minutes before the Naples police arrived. This gave him enough time to reenter the study and replace the gunshot tape with the original. This was an especially easy job since he himself was assigned to guard the room.

The Marquis de Sade's Locked Room

(1) Georges de Sade.   (2) Georges de Sade.   (3) After the supposed theft, when Georges searched the inner room.

The idea to steal occurred to Georges that Thursday morning when he and his family first saw the Napoléon letter. The naturally greedy son knew he could never persuade his father to sell a de Sade document. Stealing was the only way.

Georges set the scene by slipping the packet of money under the professor's door Friday night. On Sunday afternoon, he disguised himself with the wig and beard and rented the room, making sure to choose a seedy hotel where there was no night clerk. Then late Sunday night, Georges knocked on the professor's door. Making up some story about additional de Sade papers, Georges lured Professor Petit to the hotel room, where he proceeded to strangle him to death.

On Monday, when the professor didn't show up at the bank, Georges was ready. He bullied his way into the vault's inner room and pretended to find the professor's business card. Then, when the guard left to call the police, Georges had plenty of time to find the Napoléon letter and slip it into his clothing, leaving the dead professor to take credit for an impossible theft.

The Masked Phantom

(1) Fernando Fernas.   (2) In the first attack, he lied about the masked killer. In the second, he taped open the fire exit. (3) The first motive was robbery; the second was to give credence to his masked-killer story.

It was Fernando's first attempt at armed robbery and it went horribly wrong, resulting in Carmen Neves's death. As the out-of-work laborer knelt over his victim to take her jewelry and purse, he was caught by two witnesses. Thinking quickly, he made up a story about a masked killer. While the witnesses were off in the side alley, Fernando ran out to Rua Mariana and disposed of the gun in a garbage sack.

What Fernando didn't know at the time was that the side alley was a dead end. This naturally made him the prime suspect. The only thing preventing the police from an arrest was the lack of a gun. Once they found it and connected it to the Rua Mariana garbage, he would be exposed.

In order to bolster his story, Fernando needed to create a masked killer and to have this killer disappear in front of witnesses. When the police showed him the usher's testimony, they inadvertently gave him the timetable he needed.

Fernando entered the movie theater for an earlier show, taping open the latch to the fire-exit door. Then, a few minutes after midnight, he put on his wig, beard, and mask and hid in the alley. On the first night, nothing happened. No lone pedestrian walked through the alley during the critical period of time.

On the second night, Fernando got lucky. At 12:20, the phantom killer made himself seen by a witness, waved a gun, then disappeared into the dead-end alley. Once inside the auditorium, Fernando joined the crowd of incoming customers and took a seat. Soon after the movie started, he walked out, disposing of his disguise and a second gun in a public men's room.

River of No Return

(1) Margo and Gordon Armgaard.   (2) Fraud.   (3) Margo and Gordon killed Jan on Thursday, then had Gordon impersonate him at the new hotel.

The police would never have investigated a casual acquaintance like Gordon Armgaard had it not been for the sighting of the red Renault. They checked with the rental agency and the airlines, then questioned Gordon. He eventually confessed.

"Margo and I had been defrauding the deWys trust. When deWys grew suspicious, Margo arranged this hiking trip. The plot was all her idea. She needed an alibi and no one was even supposed to suspect me.

"We killed him Thursday on our hike, planting his body between the river rocks. You could never see it from the path. Then I put on an identical outfit and hiked back to the hotel, pretending to be deWys. That night I laid low in the room. The next morning I sneaked out to the car while Margo paid the bill. Sophia almost caught up with us, but we managed to avoid her.

"At the Vimioso hotel, no one knew the real deWys. Still, I played things safe with the sunglasses. Sophia was waiting to ambush deWys as he left. Being his wife, she knew exactly what he looked like and didn't give me a second glance.

"I planted deWys's gear on the cliff. Then I hiked along the riverbank down to the spot where we'd hidden the Renault. That same night I flew back home to Amsterdam. When the police found the body, we thought they'd assume the obvious. A lone hiker fell off a cliff and got washed downstream. Who knew the Portuguese police could be so efficient?"

Suicide Incorporated

(1) Robert Godenov. (2) Godenov, with some unwitting help from the cleaning lady. (3) The cleaning lady had found Godenov's sweetener packet containing cyanide.

A private detective working for the defense recovered the contents of the trash can by the coffee counter. In a discarded sweetener packet, he found a single grain of potassium cyanide, which wound up solving the case.

It was the second victim, Robert Godenov, who had schemed so lethally for the leadership of Yungun Best Advertising. After George Yungun died from a heart attack, Godenov murdered his replacement, Keith Best, making it look like suicide. Then, when Betina Anderson threatened to become the next CEO, Godenov plotted a second "suicide." Not only would Betina die, but in doing so, she would take the blame for the first murder.

Bob Godenov came into the office that evening to put the finishing touches on his plan. Tomorrow morning, he would give the sealed letter to Betina; tomorrow evening he would kill her. He had worked hard to make the suicide note resemble Betina's handwriting, though he was still practicing her signature. He had also stored up a precious cache of cyanide, hiding it in an artificial sweetener packet in one of his drawers.

But the cleaning lady ruined his well-laid plans. She rummaged around, found his "sweet" cyanide and was about to use it in her coffee when she was interrupted. Godenov went for his own cup of java, using the opened sweetener packet on the counter. He didn't suspect it was his own poison packet.

Godenov took a deep gulp of coffee and instantly knew. He cursed the cleaning lady, called security, then went in search of an antidote. Too late.

Twice Terminated

(1) James O'Connor.   (2) He poisoned the cold medicine which Paddy Dinsmore then stole from his room.   (3) It was a mistake; O'Connor had intended to poison his wife.

Why was the watch sixty-five minutes fast? Because it was still set on Paris time. It was James O'Connor's property, as were the diamond ring, much of the cash, and the fatal bottle of medicine. But let's start at the beginning.

O'Connor wanted to kill his wife. The reason's not important. Suffice it to say, she owned the estate and controlled much of their wealth, and he wanted out.

O'Connor bought the cold medicine, and while in his bedroom, he poisoned it. He was hoping to lay the blame on an act of consumer terrorism. But while he was off doing laps, the fired groundskeeper broke in, stole his watch, money, ring, and, since he had a cold, the repackaged medicine. This explains why Dinsmore didn't seek help. To do so would be to turn himself in as a thief. Better to tough it out and hope it was just indigestion.

When O'Connor discovered Dinsmore in his final spasms, he realized that the wrong person had gotten hold of the poison. Had he done nothing, he might have gotten away with it. But the businessman panicked. He grabbed the key, opened the trunk, retrieved the leftover medicine from Dinsmore's suitcase, and disposed of it. Then he returned to the house and called the police.

Later in the investigation, the police showed Mr. O'Connor the suspiciously expensive watch and ring. He denied ownership. But Mrs. O'Connor quickly identified both items, leading to her husband's arrest.

Oh, and why was the expensive watch sixty-five minutes off instead of exactly an hour? Like many busy people, O'Connor purposely kept his watch five minutes fast so that he wouldn't miss appointments.

Index